The Bee's Knees

McDonald's Young Writers

A collection of writings, winners in a
competition for young writers organised by
McDonald's and The O'Brien Press.

This is the second book published as a result of
this competition. The first, *The Cat's Pyjamas*,
published in 1992, was widely praised.

'a superb book of writing'
THE SUNDAY PRESS

*'excellent by any standards, and shows that Ireland
will never be short of writing talent'*
BOOKS IRELAND

*'impressive . . . fascinating insight into what
preoccupies today's young literary Ireland'*
CLAI RECOMMENDED READING LIST
for 1992 Children's Book Festival

THESE WINNING ENTRIES TO THE McDONALD'S YOUNG WRITERS
COMPETITION WERE SELECTED BY AN INDEPENDENT PANEL
OF EXPERT JUDGES OF CHILDREN'S WRITING. CHAIRPERSON OF
THE PANEL WAS DEIRDRE ELLIS-KING, DUBLIN CITY AND COUNTY
LIBRARIAN. THE JURORS WERE: MARITA CONLON-McKENNA,
AUTHOR OF CHILDREN'S BOOKS; MARY FINN, CHILDREN'S EDITOR
RTE GUIDE; DR TINA HICKEY, LINGUISTICS INSTITUTE OF IRELAND;
FINIAN O'SHEA, A TEACHER. DR PAT DONLON,
DIRECTOR OF THE NATIONAL LIBRARY OF IRELAND
ACTED AS SPECIAL ADVISOR.

ROYALTIES FROM THE SALE OF *THE BEE'S KNEES*
WILL GO TO THE ASSOCIATION FOR CHILDREN AND
ADULTS WITH LEARNING DISABILITIES

The Bee's Knees

McDonald's Young Writers

THE PRIZEWINNING
COLLECTION

Illustrations by
DONALD TESKEY

THE O'BRIEN PRESS
DUBLIN
in association with the Irish licensees of
McDonald's Restaurants of Ireland

First published 1994 by The O'Brien Press Ltd.,
20 Victoria Road, Rathgar, Dublin 6, Ireland.

10 9 8 7 6 5 4 3 2 1

British Library Cataloguing-in-publication Data
A catalogue reference for this title is available
from the British Library

Typesetting, layout, editing, design: The O'Brien Press Ltd.
Cover separations: Lithoset Ltd., Dublin
Printing: The Guernsey Press Co. Ltd.

*All applicants have been asked to verify that their entry is original work.
The publishers accept no responsibility if this requirement
has not been fulfilled.*

FOREWORD

In a child's development it is important to encourage enthusiasm, imagination and strength of thought. As young people
develop, their boundless energy needs to be harnessed to allow
them to express themselves in a unique way, such as writing.

The Irish licensees of McDonald's recognise the wealth of
talent that exists amongst Ireland's young writers, and estab-
lished the McDonald's Young Writers Competition with the
aim of encouraging and promoting the enjoyment of creative
writing. The end result was the publication in 1992 of the
best-selling *The Cat's Pyjamas*, a book written by young people
for young people.

Following its success comes *The Bee's Knees*, a compilation
of writings from the winners of this year's competition which
received a staggering twelve thousand entries.

These twelve thousand entries reflect the variety of
thoughts coming through the minds of Ireland's young people.
It is therefore most appropriate that royalties from sales of the
book will benefit the Association of Children and Adults with
Learning Difficulties.

This book has been made possible through the hard work
and cooperation of the Irish McDonald's licensees, of the
O'Brien Press and of members of the judging panel, particu-
larly Chairperson Deirdre Ellis-King.

Michael G. Mehigan

Chairman of McDonald's
Licensee Group in Ireland

A WORD FROM THE JURY

Words, words, words, a million of them, all serve to tell 'tall tales', enthuse us to travel to futuristic lands, lead us to reflect, to dream, to seek to understand. The number of entries received for the McDonald's Young Writers Project in this second year of its existence far exceeded expectations and certainly amazed those of us on the judging panel. Coming from perspectives as authors, educators and librarians, we were all agreed as to the value of participation in such projects. In reading, we were exposed to the sheer joy, enrichment and personal satisfaction which participants can receive merely from seeking to communicate, to express themselves through prose, poetry, plays and short stories. The words of the embryonic authors, ranging over a wide variety of human-interest topics of a descriptive and imaginative nature, were certainly magical and succeeded in their purpose, that of opening up for others avenues of creative expression.

Indeed, evidence of imaginative qualities and ability to use language effectively and with style to describe the ordinary and extraordinary coupled with originality in content, provided the criteria for selection of pieces for this book. Selection for publication was a difficult tast for the panellists who commend all of you, those published and unpublished, for giving us such pleasure. It is a pleasure which will be shared by all who read the work and will act, we hope, as the catalyst for some, which spurs them on to engage in the art of communicating through writing.

We thank all the participants and the many others, parents and teachers included, who encouraged their participation. All of you have made this book possible and so have merited a place in literary history.

Deirdre Ellis-King
Chairperson, Jury

Contents

A Poem Switch

GRACE LYNCH

I grope for a poem switch
In my head
But it's all dark in there
I can't find the light
To write.

My Sister Judy

DAVEY KELLEHER

Judy's a wall climber.
Can't stop her you see,
Always in trouble,
Judy ...
... and me.

The Supreme Decorator

JONATHAN MULLIN

He drove a 1978 Hi-Ace van. No wipers. One side-view mirror. One bumper tied on with bailing twine. Arthur JPT Ryan, Decorator Supreme, sure liked the luxuries in life.

Arthur was no angel by any means. He had gone on two 'holidays' to Hotel Mountjoy on the Phibsboro riviera. The first time he had stolen *Winning Streak* tickets from a shop in Claremorris. The second term was for fraud. He had painted a whole house with just one can of paint. It seems he just kept adding more and more water to the paint. He was lucky that he hadn't spent more time there because he had been getting the dole for the last five years under the name Ernest Rutherford. But to be fair to him, he had given every single penny of that to his local bookmaker.

Well, being the high-rate decorator that he was – he hadn't had work for three years – Arthur tried to keep up his image. While painting he always wore a trilby.

One Monday morning, while Arthur was doing the children's crossword in the previous day's *Sunday Press*, the 'phone rang. This was quite a shock for

Arthur. He hadn't received a 'phone call for eighteen months. It must have been a shock for the telephone too, as a big cloud of dust was shaken up by the ringing. Arthur answered the phone with the most aristocratic voice he could conjure up: 'Arthur JPT Ryan, Decorator Supreme [just about managing to pronounce "Decorator"], how may I be of assistance?'

The speaker on the other end of the line was a Mrs Dawn O'Brien. Arthur told her, tongue-in-cheek, that all his painters were out on jobs. Noticing the desperation in her voice, Arthur suggested that he himself might do the job for her at an extra charge. She gave him her address and they agreed that he would start on Wednesday.

Arthur knew that if he messed up this time his career as a decorator would be over. But if he did a good job Dawn O'Brien would be a good advertisement for him.

Arthur spent all Tuesday practising his backhand stroke. Then he took all his hens out of the Hi-Ace and stuck the steering wheel back in place.

At eight o'clock on Wednesday morning he arrived, trilby and all, on Dawn O'Brien's doorstep. For the next hour they had a good chat. Mrs O'Brien was about six foot two. Her hair-do made her seven-five. She was 65-ish, and she wore diamonds around her neck. She had lived alone in her huge house since Edward had died, she told him.

She was a daunting woman with a loud voice and Arthur was determined to do a good job.

He started painting upstairs. The carpets in the bed-rooms were about a foot thick, and because of the energy-sapping (ahem!) underfoot conditions, Arthur had to take a break for a cup of tea after only twenty minutes. However, his employer was generous (and naive) and she was only delighted to give him a break. But she said he would have to make the tea himself as she was going out shopping for one of her candlelight suppers.

Arthur switched on the kettle and sank into the giant sofa. Unfortunately for him he got too comfortable and fell into the land of nod.

He was awoken by a strange, hot, but yet cold, sweat under his collar. He opened his eyes but he

could not see anything. The whole room was cloaked in steam. He felt his way round and was finally able to open the windows. After a while most of the steam went away and he found the root of the problem. The kettle. Ah well, he would just have to start again. This time he made no mistake and five minutes later he was sitting down enjoying a cup of Brennan's Green Label.

Nothing could have prepared him for the shock he was about to receive. As he looked around the room his eyes fell on a bird cage on top of the fridge. There lay a budgie, flat out on the floor of the cage. Oh My God!! he thought, it must have been the steam that killed it.

What was he going to do? His career was over! Arthur was havin' a cow. Then he got the answer. There was only one thing for it. He searched in every press, drawer and shelf, covered the whole house and eventually found what he was looking for – Superglue.

He opened up the bird cage. Then he started to glue the budgie to his perch. When he was finished, the budgie looked full of life. Arthur took time out to admire his handiwork, then he finished his tea and ran up the stairs to start painting before Mrs O'Brien returned.

Arthur kept on painting and painting. He was on the top of the ladder painting the cornice along the ceiling when he heard a great shriek from downstairs. Because it was so sudden he fell backwards off the ladder, but thankfully the carpet was so thick that he just bounced. He quickly made his way downstairs.

There was Mrs O'Brien, a huge smile spread across her face. She was looking at the cage. She turned to Arthur and said: 'It's Edward ... he's alive!!'

Damhán Alla

N A D I N E   N Í   S C A N N L Á I N

Damhán alla,
Damhán alla,
Beag agus dubh.

Damhán alla,
Damhán alla,
Líon beag bog.

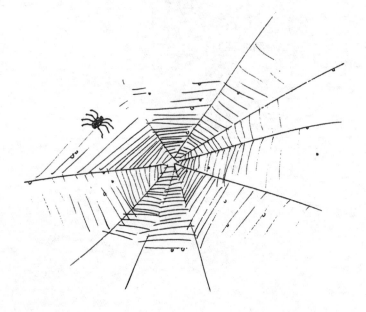

Chernobyl

AIFRIC MAC AODHA

Gan boladh
Gan blas
Gan trua
Éalaíonn rún:
Daoine bochta
Nach féidir leo
Botún a
Chealadh,
Iompraíonn siad
Spiorad briste
Anamnacha
Scriosta
Ag gach a bhfuil
Feicthe acu.
Ní throideann siad
Anseo
A thuilleadh,
Óir cailleadh
An cath
Fadó.

Planet Tron

CIARA BARDON

One night I was playing hide and seek in the woods near home with my cousins. I remember it was eight o'clock on the dot when I came to a clearing. I walked out into the middle of it, looking for a place to hide, when a beam of light fell on me. Suddenly I was being pulled upwards into the air.

I closed my eyes, and when I opened them I found myself in a large purple room. The walls were wavy, like the walls of a half-inflated bouncing castle. Then a door appeared in the wall. It slid open and an alien walked in.

The alien was green with red spots and there were only three fingers on each of his hands, and on each of his feet there were two toes. His middle finger on each hand was blue and there was a thing a bit like a trumpet on the top of his head. On each side of the trumpet there were yellow strands of what looked like wool. The only normal thing about him was that he had two eyes and a sort of slit that looked like a mouth.

Help, I thought.

'Oom palpa yolp,' he said.

'I don't understand,' I said.

'Ah, u spiks Ingilsh.'

'English, not Ingilsh,' I told him. 'Why have you brought me here?'

'My plant, Plant Tron is in great danger bekoz ze vicked Alapazocky Fulomez from Nilpod vants all us good Tronizans to be her slavez. But ve does not vant zat to 'appen.'

'What is your name?' I asked the alien.

'My name is Yolpoy,' he said. 'In Ingilsh – I meanz English – zat vould be Joseph.'

'My name is Ciara,' I said.

'Pleased to meet you,' he said.

'Now ve vill get down to de bizniz of gettingk to my dear Plant Tron. Ve vill be traflink at twice ze speed of light.'

Traflink? I thought. What in the name of goodness does traflink mean?

Then I realised he meant travelling.

'Ve are almost at my dear plant,' said Yolpoy.

'Er – Mr Yolpoy, the word is planet, not plant,' I told him.

He looked at the screen over the control-pad.

'Vell, here ve are at ze dear plan-net of Tron,' said Yolpoy. 'It is beauteevul, is it not?'

I looked at it too. The land was transparent and the sky was a sort of ivory colour. It looked strange, but I said, 'It's really very pretty.'

I saw the ground coming towards us and closed my eyes tight. Only when I felt a bump did I open them.

Yolpoy pressed a button and part of the wall swung open. The alien jumped out and gave me his hand to help me out. I noticed we were on a castle turret, or something like that.

Yolpoy ran over to a door, knocked on it, then said: 'Chaslobonskir.'

From the other side of the door came the answer: 'Sandlonidoswe.'

The door opened and we hurried inside.

'Ziz vay,' said Yolpoy and I followed him down a corridor. He stopped at a door and knocked. The door opened and we walked in.

Sitting on a purple, green and orange chair was a person like Yolpoy, except the wool was longer and her colours were different. Yolpoy bowed and I did too.

'Ziz is ze Machesty of Tron. She is ze Zalaromie,' Yolpoy whispered to me.

'Gokiliydsan hersdef kintrebd,' he said to the Zalaromie.

'Ajjxnx iwue jkshjdkcxmxn agsjyd iljuthff,' she answered.

They continued talking for a while, then Yolpoy turned to me and said: 'Ve is goingk to sort out ze battle plan.'

'What?' I said. 'I'm not going to take part in any war.'

'But you are ze only perzon that can save ze beauteevul Tron.'

He pleaded so much that I finally gave in. 'Okay, but I don't want to kill anyone.'

'Zankyou, zankyou, zankyou,' said Yolpoy.

We sat down and began to prepare our battle plan. Finally it was ready.

The next day (Earth time) we loaded the Tronizon battle ships with the secret weapons.

At three o'clock by my Earth watch, the battle ships flew out to meet Alapazocky's troops. I was in the leading ship, with Yolpoy and the Zalaromie.

Soon we met the other ships. After about an hour of fighting, we pretended we had given up. The other space soldiers turned around to tell Fulomez we had given up. As they returned to Nilpod we sneaked up behind them and our ships showered the Nilpod ones with meteorites (stage 1 of our brilliant plan). Many ships fell, but there were still plenty more left.

Next (stage 2), our ships showered them with sand.

A few ships fell, some fled, but most remained to fight.

Thirdly, the Zalaromie shouted 'Water!' and water rained down on our unfortunate opponents (stage 3). Some ships waved a white flag, but still there were others ready to fight.

By this time I was wondering if our plan would really defeat the dreaded Alapazocky Fulomez. Suddenly mud (stage four) from our spaceships showered over the remaining Nilpod ships. It must have clogged up their engines, because all the remaining ships fell down, down, down, with an eerie, piercing scream, until they had disappeared.

'Zat is ze end of ze very vicked Alapazocky Fulomez,' said Yolpoy, grinning from ear to ear. (Well, if he had ears he would have been.)

As we zapped back to Tron, Yolpoy said to me: 'All ze people of Tron are very grateful of you. You zaved our plan-net. What vould you like as ze beeg revard?'

I thought and thought. Suddenly I realised that nobody at home knew where I was! 'Please, Mr Yolpoy, as a reward could I go home?'

'Why, of course, my leedle vriend.' He spoke to the Zalaromie.

'Sfa arwev vjsb sjf oefu sxkj asdd ryt fmbj jccsj xsdsod fxghncc vjvf teo fkkgr eriroo iv vjv ksjw is b jwrhvh hfd,' she replied.

'Ze beeautivul Machesty of Tron says of course you is goink 'ome. Is there anythink else you vill be vantink?'

'Er – no,' I said. 'Wait a minute. I'd like something to remember you by, and could you do me a teeny favour?'

'Of courze.'

'Could you put me back exactly where you found me and at exactly the same time?'

'You got it.' He sounded like one of those Burger King ads you'd see on TV.

I stayed in Tron for one more Earth day, seeing the sights, and then I asked Yolpoy if I could go home.

He bundled me into his faster-than-light space-ship and, just as we were leaving, the Zalaromie turned up and got in too. She sat down beside me and buckled up her belt. I was expecting a long con-versation between the Queen and Yolpoy and then Yolpoy translating for me, but the Zalaromie had got

some gadget that translated English to Tronizon and vice versa, so on the way back to Earth the Zalaromie and I had a long chat about all sorts of things.

Finally, Earth came into sight. It took about ten minutes for Yolpoy to position himself over Ireland, and then he zoomed through the ozone layer. (Well, not actually *through* the ozone layer, but through a handy gap in it.) We hung there, floating above the earth, while we all said goodbye, and then Yolpoy beamed me back on to the ground. As soon as he was sure that I was safely on the ground, Yolpoy waved and the ship rose up into the air. I waved goodbye and then looked around me.

I was in the clearing again, but I didn't know if the time was exactly the same as when I had been picked up, because my watch was working all the time in Tron. I looked at my wrist to check the time, and on my wrist I saw a bracelet. On it was a picture of Yolpoy and the Zalaromie.

Well, I thought, Yolpoy kept two of his promises. Now, will he keep the third, I wonder?

I didn't have to wonder for long. I heard my cousin, Becky call: 'Coming, ready or not, keep your place or you'll be caught.'

I was back in the right time.

'Good old Yolpoy,' I thought.

Diary of a War Horse

P E T E R   H U G H E S

Standing five foot at the shoulders and with a strong, muscular body, I was one of the finest horses in the French Cavalry. I belonged to Pierre Lacroix, a General of Napoleon. I can well remember those days of war and bloodshed.

The first time I rode into battle was in Egypt. There was lots of blood and I was nearly deafened by the noise of those cannons mixed with the terrible din of men shouting. I tried to concentrate and do what Pierre told me to do, but I was so terrified and dazed that I nearly got my head shot off. It was awful.

At last, when the battle ended and the Egyptians surrendered, I was brought back to France and tied up in Napoleon's stables. Pierre went inside and occasionally I heard cries of '*Vive La France*' and '*Vive l'Empereur*'. Then, I heard a voice beside me in the dark stable. It was Napoleon's fine horse. We became good friends and he taught me a lot about waging war.

Next time I went into battle I was better prepared. I skilfully brought my master to victory and I was proud. I was beginning to get used to winning. Then we attacked Moscow, in Russia. We won easily but the Russians retreated and destroyed everything on their way. We hadn't enough supplies and we had to give up. The winter came early and many died from cold and starvation. Somehow, Pierre and I managed to get back. Out of six hundred thousand men only a hundred thousand made it back. We were defeated a few more times and Napoleon was exiled to the Island of Elba. The barrack-stables became my permanent home. It was strange not fighting wars anymore. Life was not as exciting, but all the same it was peaceful and pleasant.

One day who should I meet in the stables but Napoleon's horse. This meant that Napoleon himself must be back. I was right. For in two weeks I was taken along with all the other horses out of the barracks, to where a massive army was waiting. We were mounted and we set off towards Belgium. The year was 1815. At Waterloo we met a large British-German army. We went into battle but we were defeated and Pierre was killed.

That was the last time I went to battle. But now as I look back on it I can still see all those battles in my head. Now I am old and weak, but I have learned one thing – although there is some glory, make no mistake, war is practically hell on earth.

The Troll

MICHAEL PATTEN

Beware of the crafty troll,
That slyly lies in wait,
To bring you into his deep hole,
And put you on his plate.

His blood is black and boiling hot,
He gurgles ghastly groans,
He'll cook you in his dinner pot,
Your skin, your flesh, your bones.

He'll catch your arms and grab your legs,
And grind you to a pulp,
And swallow you like scrambled eggs,
Gobble gobble gulp.

The Mechanical Drawing Poem

GEOFFREY GRAY

I sit at my desk, regarding the comforting lines
  on my page.
Perfectly straight, beautiful in their perfection,
They criss-cross each other
To form shapes and projections.
Straight lines, right angles,
No uncertainty here!
It is either right or wrong, black or white,
No in-betweens or greys.
And when I finish, I regard my work with pride:
A building, one hundred feet high, lies passive
  on my page.

Ionsaí Ningach!

DARA DE BÚRCA

Mo bhreithlá a bhí ann agus dúirt mo Dhaidí liom go bhfaigheadh sé rud éigin speisialta mar bhronntanas dom. Bhí sceitimíní orm an lá ar fad. Bhí mé ag iarraidh a thomhas céard a gheobhadh sé dom.

Nuair a tháinig sé abhaile bhí pacáiste mór ina lámh aige. Thug sé dom é agus níor chuir mé aon am amú á oscailt. Cad a bhí ann ach dioscaí agus '*joystick*' speisialta. Dúirt m'athair liom go bhfuair sé iad i siopa nua-oscailte ar Shráid an Tulaigh. Dúirt sé freisin go ndúirt fear an tsiopa leis gur cluiche nua a bhí iontu a bhí díreach ar fáil sa tír seo. Chuir mé mo ríomhaire ar siúl agus chuir mé an chéad diosca isteach ann.

Tar éis cúpla soicind tháinig an t-ainm suas ar an scáileán: *Neart na Ninga*. Ansin dúirt sé an *joystick* a chur ag obair. Thug sé ordú diosca eile a chur isteach. Chuir mé isteach é. Nóiméad ina dhiaidh sin thosaigh an cluiche. Ba bhall de na gardaí speisialta mise agus bhí orm stop a chur le cumann Ninga a bhí ag déanamh damáiste do chathair éigin. Bhí ormsa mo ghunna speisialta a úsáid chun na créatúir a mharú.

Bhí an cluiche ag dul ar aghaidh go breá go dtí gur shroich mé leibhéal a dó. Go tobann tharla rud éigin an-ait. D'imigh m'fhear a bhí ar an scáileán as radharc

agus nuair a tharla sé sin bhraith mé an-trom! Bhí an
t-arm go léir a bhí ar m'fhear á iompar agamsa anois.
Agus freisin d'athraigh an *joystick* go dtí gunna ait.
Díreach ansin thosaigh an slua Ningach ag léim as an
scáileán! Bhíodar go léir ag dul amach an doras agus
fiú tríd na fuinneoga. Nuair a bhí siad go léir imithe
léim créatúr amháin eile as an scáileán. Ní Ninga a bhí

ann; chuir sé an bás i gcuimhne dom! 'Is mise Fordre,' ar seisean. 'Ná cuir aon cheist orm go fóill – níl a lán ama fágtha. Chun an gunna a úsáid brúigh an cnaipe dearg ar do thaobh dheis. Brúigh an ceann gorm agus beidh tú in aice leis an chéad ghrúpa eile Ningach. Brúigh an ceann buí agus beidh gach rud reoite. Ní mharóidh an gunna iad; tabharfaidh sé ar ais isteach sa chluiche iad. Tá an scáileán ag taispeáint cá bhfuil siad. Imigh anois mar tá an slua Ningach sin chun a lán damáiste a dhéanamh muna mbeireann tú orthu in am.'

Go tobann chuaigh Fordre as radharc agus ní raibh tásc ná tuairisc air. Rith mé amach i dtreo an bhaile. Chonaic mé an chéad cúpla ceann ag briseadh fuinneog ar an bpríomhshráid. Chuaigh mé chucu agus bhrúigh mé an cnaipe dearg. Bhí siad thuas san aer anois. Cheapfá go raibh siad á n-iompar ag rud éigin, ach chomh luath is a bhí siad san aer chuadar as radharc. Is dócha gur imigh siad isteach sa ghunna agus as sin go dtí an diosca.

Ansin d'fhéach mé suas an tsráid. Bhí seachtar Ninga ag déanamh a lán damáiste do charr. Rith mé chucu agus shlog mé isteach sa ghunna iad. Bhí deich gcinn fágtha fós ar seachrán. Bhrúigh mé an cnaipe gorm agus go tobann bhí mé cúpla méadar ó ghrúpa eile díobh. Bhí siad ag scriosadh rompu i siopa bróg. Anois bhrúigh mé an cnaipe buí. Nuair a rinne mé seo bhí gach rud reoite. Shiúil mé chucu agus leag mé mo lámh orthu – d'imigh siad as radharc. Chuir an gunna in iúl dom nach raibh ach ceann amháin eile le fáil. D'fhéach mé ar an Radar. Thaispeáin sé an Ninga deireanach san ollmhargadh ag cur eagla ar dhaoine. Bhrúigh mé an cnaipe gorm agus bhí mé díreach in aice leis an Ninga seo. Bhí rud éigin aisteach faoi, áfach. Bhí a lán airm air, freisin. Bhí sé an-ard agus d'fhéach sé an-láidir. Ghlaoigh mé air agus d'fhéach sé i mo threo. Bhrúigh mé an cnaipe dearg ach níor oibrigh sé – bhí orm troid leis ón tús.

An t-aon rud a bhí cearr leis an Ninga mór ná go raibh sé mall. Rith mé isteach sa siopa crua-earraí agus rug mé ar rópa mór fada. Rith mé ar ais go dtí an Ninga agus rith mé timpeall agus timpeall ar a chosa leis an rópa. Tar éis cúpla nóiméad thit an Ninga. Ansin bhrúigh mé an cnaipe buí agus bhí sé reoite. D'úsáid mé an cnaipe dearg chun é a thabhairt ar ais sa chluiche.

Chuaigh mé abhaile agus chuir mé gach rud ar ais sa bhosca. Chuir mé glaoch ar an siopa nua ach ní bhfuair mé aon fhreagra. Chuaigh mé síos go dtí an siopa ach bhí sé scriosta – is dócha gur scrios an slua Ningach é.

Chuaigh mé abhaile agus chuir mé an bosca faoi ghlas sa seomra folamh agus tá sé fós ansin inniu.

Light

R U T H   M O R R I S S E Y

And then the lights faded. Vanished. Gone. No puff of smoke, no round of applause, no encore. Just there one moment and then – gone. And the darkness reigned. And in a funny sort of way, if things could seem funny in this state of being, she missed the lights. Even though every excruciatingly dazzling dart of brightness sent her brain hurtling through unknown realms of her skull, and the pain seemed far too much to bear, she missed them. They were something to measure her brain's consciousness by. But now, there was nothing. Nothing except the throbbing and pulsing of something, somewhere in her body. And after some time – minutes, hours, days? – even that faded.

* * *

The smell of nothing-in-particular was bothering Stem. That indescribable, unique smell of nothing-in-particular that all hospitals, without exception, have. Even those new, hotel-like hospitals that try so hard to be different, with their casual, friendly, 'This is the best place to be, Mr Smith' approach – even those 'unhospitals' have that smell, and it was bothering Stem.

A lot of things bothered Stem. Like her name, for example. She hadn't got a reasonable explanation for her parents' choice of name. They were just *like* that. Experimental people. They probably stuck the name on her just to see if a person called Stem could actually survive in the world. They were *that* kind of people. They once named one of their dogs Honeyyoghurteggflip – just to see. Just to see what? Her embarrassment when she had to call the animal down from their new neighbour's roof? Yeah, that was a good example of her mother and father's attitude to life. They'd sit back and watch everyone else living, and if there was a remote possibility of making life more difficult for somebody, or more amusing for themselves, they would. So that was how she ended up with a name like 'Stem'. Her parents weren't poets or artists. They never said: 'The stem is the most important part of the flower, supplying it with life. So, too, you are the most vital part of our lives, darling, filling us with pride and admiration.' No way. Nothing like that. She was just called Stem because she wasn't called 'Scissors' or 'Atom'.

The smell of dinner wafted down the corridor. Hospital dinner. Always potatoes and yellow carrots and indistinguishable meat with sauce. Never pizza. Never pasta. Always this anonymous 'dinner'. Stem's stomach growled at the thought. She shifted position in the uncomfortable plastic chair. Think sad, she told herself, and looked at the ground solemnly. Staring at a spot of black something on the floor, she felt a guilty sense of indifference. Indifference at her best friend's state of health. Her very, very best friend. Stem commanded herself to think seriously about the situation. Her good friend Amy was in a coma in a room around the corner. Things were not looking good for her – in other words, she was going to die. And Stem didn't give a toss. She probably would have felt as bad if the disco on Thursday had been cancelled. Honestly. And even when she thought about all the fun they would never have again – no double-dating, no sleep-overs, no hour-long telephone calls, no hairdressing sessions – even when she thought about that, no tear trickled down her cheek. And it wasn't that reality hadn't hit her yet. She understood everything, and felt nothing. Nothing except the guilt caused by this lack of emotion.

*　　*　　*

Amy wanted to go. Go anywhere. Go to school. Go to the toilet. She just wanted to be out of this state of vegetation. This was *that* place. That place between Heaven and Hell. Somewhere beginning with P. Yes, this was it. She was dead. And she'd discovered that people were praying to the wrong God. God's real name was John. What seemed to be days ago, she had heard someone say, 'Insert it into the lower arm, John', and she had felt a hosepipe being stuck into her arm and all her gooey inside bits flowing in and out of it. It seemed odd – she had spent all of her life, well, bits of it anyway, praying to him, and now all he did was stick a huge big pipe in her arm and leave her in this dark, lonely P place, wondering.

* * *

Stem's legs had gone beyond numbness, and were now progressing towards the dough state. When she applied pressure to them they buckled at the knees. She was about to crawl over to the coffee machine when she heard voices approaching from around the bend in the corridor. Amy's parents were discussing their daughter's condition with a young doctor. The same old story. Getting weaker. And weaker. Amy's mother looked dreadful. She was as white as a ghost and tears streaked her face. Her father was being a comfort to his wife, but Stem could see his pain too. Tension and worry were painted in every line on his face and as he put his arm around his wife's shoulders, Stem wondered whether it was really to comfort his wife or to reassure himself. He had almost lost one member of his family, his only child, and Stem understood his need to know that the only other member of his beloved family was still by his side.

* * *

The lights were returning. Amy waited for the searing stabs of pain, but they didn't come. This was a different light. A very different light. It was the whitest, most peaceful thing she had ever seen. And suddenly she felt a love more overpowering than any love she had experienced before, and a happiness more complete and fulfilling than her happiest moment in everyday life. And life suddenly seemed so far away. And her heart seemed to laugh with joy. And her body was just a discarded plaything, a costume to wear for five minutes of the day that was forever. And everything was perfect.

The Orchard

EIMEAR McNALLY

Orchard breathes,
listens, waits.
The voice of my memory
speaks without words,
of a time I hope
I have not lost,
of a place I need
when I'm not there,
of people I love
but have not told,
of finding fallen apples
in the rich, long grass.

The Bee Story

STEPHEN O'BRIEN

It was a sunny day.

The bee was reading a book. A cat came along and made the bee drop the book. The book dropped on the cat's head and it slid down the cat's neck onto the cat's body, then it slid down his tail. He fell over with fright and fell asleep. Then when he woke up he didn't know what he was. He thought he was a bee. He tried to buzz but he couldn't. He tried to fly but he couldn't. He tried to collect honey from the flowers but he squashed them. He tried to say Ouch, but he said Mieeow. He knew then that he was a cat. He was very happy then and he lived happily ever after.

A Glorious Victory

J A M E S   B O W E N

A cold, red light flared in the distance for a moment, over the shellholes, the corpses and the gutted bodies of tanks, and then died away, leaving the battlefield in silent, morose darkness.

Tower pushed the hatch open on its rusted, complaining hinges and put his head out. 'What was that?'

'Unexploded shell going off,' said the Captain, shuffling some cards and passing them around the ammunition crate upended on the LAV's deck, to Godhead, Yevsky and me. 'That, or the Starskiy have found themselves a mortar.'

'The Starskiy,' I said. 'I've heard of them. Who exactly are they?'

'Anti-New Belarussian guerrillas,' said Yevsky. 'We had a band of them attack us before...' Lost for words, he gestured with his hands across the grounded, abandoned LAV-25's interior to indicate the torn and bullet-ploughed field outside as well as us – a sorry group, jaded remnants of the armies who had fought that day, each of us allied to some, sworn enemies to others. 'Before this.'

'They're calling it Bastev-Donar,' said Godhead. He took a card from the pile the captain had made.

'After the village, like.'

'If it's any consolation,' said the Captain, half-heart-edly keeping the cards warm, 'the Starskiy attacked a whole bunch of depleted American units over Slati way. They're just bandits, opportunists. They've no real political agenda.'

Tower ducked down into the cabin out of the wind outside. 'Bastev-Donar's not there any more, you know.' It was true; the Perostrians had razed the town during the battle, before it was captured.

'I heard,' I said, 'they were Muslims, you know, the whole *jihad* thing. Fundamentalists.'

'Radical fundamentalists,' Tower intoned, before putting his head out of the hatch again.

'That's stupid,' said Godhead, exchanging the cards in his hand with vague disinterest before laying them down and leaning back against the hull of the tank.

'You can't be a radical fundamentalist. Stands to reason.'

'Oh, I rather think you can,' said Yevsky. 'Has anyone a dictionary?'

'The US Army considers literature a dead weight,' muttered the Captain. I thought I could detect a note of sarcasm in his voice.

'Right, I mean, war's not about books, is it?' said Godhead helpfully. 'Some Red comes up – saving your presence, Yevsky – you don't want to learn about his frigging sociological history, do you? You want to wrap his guts around his spine.'

'A good point,' came Tower's voice.

The captain whispered something like 'Hark at him,' and there was silence for some time.

Eventually I said, 'Turn on the radio there, sir, for the report.'

The Captain leaned forward wearily and flicked on the wireless. As he tuned across the band, there were a few snatches of faint, static-scarred gibberish, disembodied cries in the distance. When he finally found a station, it was the much-maligned propaganda organ, the Voice of New Belarus. 'Devil and damnation,' murmured the Captain, and he reached to extinguish the radio.

Yevsky put his hand out. 'No,' he said. 'We may as well hear what my bungling countrymen have to say.'

'The New Belarussian Army today met the armies of the West outside the tiny Perostrian village of Bastev-Donar,' began the announcer in a thick Slavic accent veneered with stereotypical American suavity.

'Though the capitalist forces considered this battle a foregone conclusion, they were received with fearsome resistance from our soldiers. The fighting was long and hard, but in the end, Field Marshal Anders Begowicz and the army of Neobelarus could claim a glorious victory ...'

'Glorious victory?!' Godhead screamed. He hit the table with his fist and the deck of cards bounced into disarray across the floor. 'Bastard! We won, and he knows it! We've got the dirty little Pole north of the Königstadt parallel ...'

'There are no winners in war,' said Yevsky sternly. 'Everyone loses: life, youth, innocence. Each side inflicts pain on the other until one can bear it no more, and then that side lets the other put its flag in the ground.'

The Captain sighed. 'I think there are winners and losers,' he said. 'There must be, because only losers ever have glorious victories. Winners win, so they have to stand among the dead and be held responsible, and see what they've done; losers just hobble home to be decorated and boast about their bravery. Tower,' he called.

Tower bent down into the interior. 'Yes, sir?' he said.

'Would you say we had a glorious victory?' asked the Captain.

Tower stood up for a moment, then his head dropped into view once more. 'To be honest, sir? No, sir. More of a Pyrrhic victory, really, you know? In fact, just lookin' at the battlefield, you couldn't tell who won at all.'

The captain whispered something like 'Hark at him,' and there was silence for some time.

Fat Cat

NIAMH REILLY

I had a cat.
He never could run,
He was much too fat,
So he sat and he sat
And he sat ...

Braces

LINDA MURPHY

The question is, are they worth it? Is the deformation of your mouth, the humiliation of wearing retainers and the name-calling worth it? In the end, what will you have to show for all your pain and suffering? Yes, you've got it, a mouth full of straight, square china that may get you into the Miss World Contest, but that's about all.

The first painful experience you have to go through is a trip to the extraordinarily unfriendly orthodontist. After my first visit I had renamed Dr B Jones, a prim and proper 5 foot 3 inch doctor in a well-starched white coat, HITLER.

It was introductions first, a little chit chat – 'And what year are you in?' 'First year' 'Oh that's nice' – and then straight down to business. I opened my mouth and she was in there for the next hour. Suction, drills, needles, the works. I got a lot of 'Now this will not hurt.' Then AHH! Pain! What that lady's definition of hurt is, I'll never know.

When you do finally get out of that dreaded chair, your mouth won't close because it's been open for so long. You have to firmly shut it with your hands as you now have a few more metal bits in your mouth than you went in with.

The first piece of apparatus she attaches to you is the Retainer, which is also the beginning of the name-calling and humiliation. 'Bunny' suddenly becomes your new name, as the front wires are shaped like rabbits' ears. You slurp, stutter, and spit for the first few weeks, and start holding conversations with yourself, as people either can't understand you or they just don't want an early-morning shower of spit. When you take the thing out you must always do it discreetly in the toilet, as you wouldn't know what might come out with it. It mainly depends on what you have eaten beforehand, as food tends to get caught between the upper plate and the roof of your mouth. The worst thing I've found stuck up there was spaghetti Bolognese, yesterday's dinner.

Next to come are the reliable old Train Tracks. You start hearing a lot of 'choo choos' around the yard and the boys rename you 'Metal Mouth'. Beautiful, I know. On top of all this, there is a lot of pain involved, as these contraptions are pulling back your teeth.

At times it is very sore to eat, and you get pains in your joints, especially after the Horse Halter – I mean the Night Brace. This piece of equipment starts inside your mouth in the form of a metal semicircle, and comes out of the mouth to attach onto a cloth head-piece. The idea is that you sleep wearing it. Sleep – ha! More like stare at the ceiling hour after hour, night after night, until finally you take the dumb thing off and hope that the dentist will not notice.

There are actually some good points about having braces, though not many. In the beginning you get loads of icecream and jelly and soft sweets – this lovely innocent child can't eat any solid hard food as it's too sore – but all good things must come to an end, and with braces and a deadly dentist, good things come to an end very fast. She somehow knows,

in that psychic mind of hers, that all you have been eating is lovely junkfood, so she calls Mammy right away and ruins your cover. She tells her that statistically after three days – *not* three weeks – you are easily and painlessly able to eat your tasty greens. Lucky me!

Well, now I've come to the end of my story about braces, and I'm afraid I can't tell you if they are worth it or not. I still have crooked teeth and an over-bite, but if you write to me in two years' time I should be able to tell you either that my teeth are straight or that I've killed the lovely Hitler before she could finish the treatment.

(*Names have been changed to protect identities.*)

My Grandad Frank's Day

KAREN LEONARD

We started off early on that Sunday morn,
A west wind blowing cold across the Midlands,
Deserted towns in scattered showers,
Brief pictures on a January day and the radio on, just
    killing time.
Onward bound, a winding road that seemed so long
    from my house to old Kilcormac.
Just a point along the western way,
On our journey down to my Grandad Frank's day.

In the pale winter sun we huddled around,
'Sorry for your trouble'
'It's a happy release'
Words that don't mean much when death is in town,
And the toll of the bell in the icy wind played a cold
Lonely tune to remind us of our own mortality,
Which is only a heart-beat away.
Don't you know nothing ever lasts,
Nothing was meant to.
So here we are all gathered around for my Grandad
    Frank's day.

We stood in the graveyard frozen with fear and cold,
Winter faces lost in a wilderness of pain and anguish,
A legacy that death leaves us with.

*Out of our sadness a robin appeared from the cold blue
    horizon,*
Hopped and bopped beside an open grave.
A gift from heaven, perhaps, to show us the way,
That this end is just a beginning and what we lose
We gain in another life
Which in this time of ours we can find no trace of.
I'll always remember our robin when I think back in time
To my Grandad Frank's day.

I have fond memories of childhood days,
Football in the garden with my country cousins,
And my Grandad Frank watching,
His pipe gently puffing,
A grandfather enriched by what his grandchildren might be.
In years to come the dreams may come true,
What more can anyone ask for?
I thought of all these things on my Grandad Frank's day.

I wish you all well and I thank you for your kindness.
Although I spoke to few,
I felt enriched,
I felt a part of,
For that I am grateful.
As I sat in that bright sunny kitchen amidst relatives
And friends from far and from near,
I guess that just being there was the best I could do,
I'm just glad I went all that way for my
Grandad Frank's day.

(Dedicated to my loving Grandad Frank Currams, RIP)

The Fight

A N D R E W   T O F T

He was coming from the cafeteria. I was running to meet a friend when I bumped into him. He fell back clumsily, and I retreated to see who I had hit. It was he, the fellow who broke Larry's leg, gave Pete stitches above his right eye and told the Principal to go jump. He stared down at me piercingly. I was terrified of the fierce structure which advanced slowly towards me, like a wild beast preparing for the kill. My thoughts were washing around inside my mind. Should I stay and fight? Should I run? Would he catch me? Would he leave me alone? Would he beat me up?

By now a large crowd had gathered. He stood there for a while as though measuring me up. Then, without any warning whatsoever, he punched me brutally, sending me with a thump onto the hard, unsympathetic floor. I got up, dazed and shaken. He struck again, this time hitting me on the nose with a sharp right, which caused an echo of pain to run through my body. Then I felt the pressure in my nose. It felt like a dam breaking. I instantly knew what it was. The mongrel had cut me. I was bleeding. I threw myself at him and we both fell back onto a table. The thrilled crowd jumped about and squealed and laughed. Then a teacher, followed quickly by three more, came galloping into the room. They pulled him off me and dragged him away. Just before he left he shouted back, 'After school, you little runt.'

A teacher told him to shut up or he would be sent to the Principal's office. This didn't seem to worry him, and he brandished a finger. 'RIGHT!' shouted the teacher and marched him off to the Principal.

I went to the school nurse, who quickly sorted out my nose and gave me the usual lecture about fighting. I tried hard to explain the goings on of lunchtime but she wouldn't listen, so I picked up my bag and drifted out of her office. I knew, and so did everybody else, that he would beat me to a pulp straight after school. I couldn't concentrate for the rest of the day thinking about what he might do to me.

Bing bing bing – there they go, the bells that mark my death, I thought. I left through the side door, hoping to avoid him and sneak home. So what if he would get me the next day, I was free today and that was all that counted. No such luck, however – there he was, waiting. He had anticipated my every move. The crowds were there, as usual. I turned and walked in another direction, but a group of boys met me. I knew who they were – his accomplices Simon Kellagher, Pete Moroney and Geoffrey Cartright. There was only one way to go and it meant coming face-to-face with him.

'Come on now, or are you chicken?'

'No!' I knew I should add to my answer for the crowd's enjoyment. I should pretend to be brave. But

I could not, I was too scared. I made my way back very slowly. He loomed in front of me, serious as ever. We stood facing each other and I realised with a sinking feeling that he was at least a foot taller than me, and hugely built. His massive arms hung rigid by his sides, bulging with muscles. At the bottom of these arms were clenched fists, ready for combat. One of the crowd pushed me and I flew into him. My head hit his chest with a thump and before I could react I felt him grip me. He lifted me about two feet into the air and threw me head first towards the crowd. I did not want to cry again but it was so hard to hold back. I was petrified. I was ready to tell a teacher. Yes, I would wreck my reputation and break the schoolboy code. It

was better than getting my head kicked in by some over-sized ape.

The torture wasn't over yet though. Grabbing me again he held me up with one hand, striking a vicious blow to my face with the other. The pain, oh the pain. It was excruciating. I cried. This delighted him, and dropping me he threw his arms up in victory. The crowd cheered. I lay there, broken and sobbing, hoping it was a dream, but it was not. The crowd chanted: 'FINISH HIM, FINISH HIM.' He spat on me and gave me a good hard kick in the stomach. Then he left, laughing an evil laugh. My friend helped me up as the crowd dispersed. I stopped crying. I felt a bit better now that it was all over. I picked up my bag and made my way across the playing field. Then without even thinking I turned and shouted out at the top of my voice, 'YOU TWO-FACED GIT!'

He turned and looked, but that was all he did. Everybody heard me and again they cheered. I had taken his victory from him and he knew it. He would kill me tomorrow, but so what.

My Daddy

FERGUS MONNELLY

Daddy is very good because he likes me. He shows me new things on the computer, so he likes me very much. Sometimes I win football games with him. Daddy is not able to cook because he never learned. He didn't let me into the shop when he was getting the new sink because I was running around in the other shops. Once he showed me how to charge my remote control car. Once he showed me a completely new computer game which was 'Wolf 3D'. Sometimes he gives me treats.

My Baby Sister

BENJAMIN BREEN

I have a baby sister
Who's only five months old.
She's the eighth child in the house now
And the last one ... so I'm told.

She has pink toes and rose-bud lips
And two big cute blue eyes,
She smiles with dimples in her rosy cheeks
And when she gets cranky she cries.

I love my baby sister,
She's chubby and nice to squeeze,
She's as squashy as pink marshmallow,
And as smooth as creamy cheese.

And when we're playing peek-a-boo,
Her chin goes up and down,
But if any loud noise should startle her
She'll give you a quizzical frown.

She is a lovely baby,
But I really must be fair,
If she gets her hand upon your head,
You'll wish you had no hair.

(Dedicated to my sister Sarah.)

Old

MAUDE FAHY

I am old,
my face is like a shrivelled flower,
the pretty petals have fallen off me,
I love the silent Mass days,
I see all the beauty of heaven
before me.

Snow White and the Seven Dwarfs

SARA HAYES

Once upon a time, there was a young hippie called Snow White (her parents had been hippies back in the sixties, hence the unusual name). Snow's mother had died soon after she was born and a few years later her father remarried.

Snow's stepmother had always wanted a daughter who dressed normally and was bright in school. Snow didn't fit the bill, so when Step-Mum, (that was what Snow called her) heard of a local modelling competition, she hoped that this would be the very thing to change her.

So Snow, despite her loud and rather vulgar protests, was dragged off to a modelling agency. There a number of women examined Snow from all sides, and made various comments about her appearance. Soon Snow began to look forward to the competition.

Then one of the women remarked to Step-Mum, 'You'd stand a good chance in the competition yourself, even though they'd all be younger than you.'

Step-Mum had always dreamed of being a model, and now that the chance was being offered to her she wasn't going to let that brat, Snow White, spoil her chances.

When they arrived home, Step-Mum turned to Snow, and in cold, even tones, informed her: 'I've decided I don't want you entering that competition at your age. I'm going to enter instead.'

'You can't stop me!' shouted Snow.

'That's what you think,' replied her stepmother. 'If you enter that competition, your spot cream will conveniently disappear the day before the judging. You won't stand a chance!'

Snow stared open-mouthed at her evil stepmother, then she turned and ran into her room, flung herself onto the bed and started crying. After about an hour of feeling sorry for herself, Snow made up her mind. She was going to run away.

She packed a few things into her bag and took all the money she had. Then she crept silently out the back door and rode off on her bike.

Snow decided to go up north. She was only seventeen, but she was sure she could find work somewhere.

She headed towards the train station and got there just in time to catch the five o'clock train. Once the train started moving, Snow soon fell asleep. She woke with a start a few hours later and realised they had stopped.

Then the driver's voice came booming over the speakers: 'I regret to announce that the rails have been closed due to dangerous conditions. All fares will be refunded.'

Snow followed the stream of passengers off the train and into the town. The night was cold and wet, and there was a strong gale blowing. She didn't fancy sleeping out in the open so she started looking for hotels. In every hotel she went to she was told they were sorry, but they were full up.

She was beginning to feel desperate when she spotted an open shed in somebody's back garden. There didn't seem to be anyone around, so in she went.

In the morning, she was woken by the sound of voices. She opened her eyes and saw a cluster of heads looking down at her.

'She's awake!' cried one excitedly, then shut up as the others glared at him.

'Be quiet!' said another, who seemed to be in charge. Then he turned to Snow and demanded angrily, 'Who are you, and what are you doing in our shed?'

Snow answered defiantly, 'My name is Snow White, and I spent the night here because I had nowhere else to go!'

'Don't you have a home?' he asked, his voice gentler this time. On the verge of tears, Snow told him the story.

'I ... um ... I suppose you could stay here for a while, that's if you want to, of course,' he said.

'Oh, I'd love to!' exclaimed Snow.

'Well, I suppose you'd like some breakfast?' he asked her. 'Come into the house, you must be freezing.'

It was only as they were going into the house that Snow noticed that they were all much smaller than she was, and inside the house all the furniture was tiny. While they were eating breakfast she asked them about it.

Immediately they all started talking at once. 'I can't

hear anything if you all talk together,' said Snow. So they started, one at a time to tell the story.

'There is a big nuclear power plant not far from here,' began the first.

'There was a huge explosion when we were small,' chipped in another.

'Ssh,' said the first one, 'I'm the person telling the story. Well, anyway, after this explosion we all stopped growing. The doctor said it was because of exposure to high levels of radiation. The nuclear plant gave us jobs and this house, so we wouldn't tell anyone about it.'

Snow was very happy living with the dwarfs. She didn't go out much though, because she was still afraid Step-Mum would find her. And then, one day, she did.

Snow never knew how Step-Mum had discovered where she was, but one night, when everyone was asleep, Step-Mum broke into the house. She crept silently into Snow's room and, laughing to herself, she swapped Snow's bottle of Clearasil for something else. Then, as silently as she had come in, she left the house and nobody knew about it until the next morning.

Snow stared at her reflection in horror. Her face was a mass of ugly, red pimples. She guessed at once what had happened. She grabbed the mirror off the wall, put it outside in the hallway and locked the door.

Soon one of the dwarfs, Dopey, came to call her for breakfast.

'I'm not going out looking like this,' she shouted.

'But, Snow, you always look lovely,' said Dopey.

'You haven't seen my spots, have you?' she wailed.

One by one, the dwarfs came to plead with Snow to come out, but to no avail. Eventually they just left her breakfast by the door and went to work.

She stayed in her room for over three weeks. Then one day, as she was staring out the window, a handsome young head-banger named Deff rode by on a Harley-Davidson. When he saw Snow at the window he fell totally in love with her.

He ran up to the house and rang the doorbell. Happy, who was depressed for once, answered it. 'Hello, can I help you?'

'Well, em, I was wondering who that girl in the window is?' said Deff.

'Oh, that's Snow White,' Happy replied.

'Can I talk to her?' asked Deff.

'Well, she hasn't come out of her room for almost a month,' said Happy sadly, 'but I suppose there's no harm in trying.'

Deff went up to her room and knocked on the door.

'Go away,' said Snow.

'My name is Deff,' said Deff. 'I'd like to talk to you.'

Snow opened the door and came out. Her jaw dropped when she saw Deff.

'I know we've only just met, but I love you and I want you to marry me,' said Deff.

'Oh, Deff,' Snow said quietly, 'I'd love to.'

Snow never saw her stepmother again after that. She and Deff got married and they lived happily ever after.

Crann

GEMMA BLANCHE

Istigh sa pháirc,
Ag síneadh suas sa spéir,
Níos airde ná na tithe,
Ag breathnú orainn go léir.
Géaga móra, láidre,
Duilleoga ag luascadh sa ghaoth,
Fréamhacha fada, buana,
Go domhain sa chré.
Oíche na stoirme móire,
Gálaí ag scriosadh gach croí,
Mo chrann álainn caillte,
Ar an talamh ina luí!

The Love of my Life

MUIREANN PRENDERGAST

It was dark. A cold, skinning breeze was turning my hair askew, ruining the hour which I had spent putting mousse on it. My fingers were raw with the cold. I glanced in a nearby window, pretending to be interested in the wide selection of dandruff shampoo and hair lice remedies, as I secretly took a look at myself. I looked terrible. My eyes resembled those of a St Bernard and my face was as white as the contents of a Tipp-Ex bottle. Slowly but surely I made my way to the town hall, where the group which I had joined would be meeting. It was my first visit.

I climbed the stairs in a languid fashion, following the arrows up to the meeting room. I walked in, noticed that I was only the fifth person to arrive, and slumped down beside an obese woman who seemed to be in a world of her own. My nose tickled – I had a cold – and I longed to blow it, but from past experience of listening to others blowing their noses, I decided to put up with it. A little while later, when the room was nearly full, the group leader Bill Buckley stood up and formally started the meeting.

'Hi there! How are ye all doing?' he asked in a sensitive tone of voice.

People nodded and said that it was a pretty good week.

'Okay, that's fab!' smiled Bill. 'Right, let's start. As you all know this is the fifty-seventh meeting of the Listening Group, where we all hear everyone's problems and offer helpful advice and therapy. Today we have a new member.'

'Oh my God, it's me,' I gasped. The whole group looked towards me. A warm tight feeling was groping its way up my neck. I could feel my face going red. Think of something to say quickly, you twit, I said to myself. They're all looking at you!

'Um ... hi there!' was all I could come up with.

Bill continued: 'This is Clodagh Boyle, and she's joining us today. Say "Hi" everybody!'

'Hi!' they all answered in unison.

'Okay, Clodagh, since this is your first day here, how would you like to stand up and tell us all about your problem?' His voice was very sympathetic.

I stood up, shaking with fear, but I knew that I was doing the right thing. I had to get it off my chest and tell somebody – it was the only way.

I cleared my throat and prepared to unravel my story. 'Well,' I started, 'it all began when I was about six or seven. Maybe seven. We had just got a new dog, a labrador in fact, his name was Charlie. Anyway, Mam started to buy Charlie dogfood and dog biscuits – you know, Bonios and the like – and it was my job to give the Bonios to Charlie. Nothing weird about that, I hear you say. Well, every night I used to watch, with great interest, Charlie wolfing down the Bonios. He

seemed to love them and he always wanted more. I often wondered what they tasted like, and then one day I dared to try.

'Oh! It seems like yesterday the day I had my first Bonio. I remember taking Charlie's packet and sneaking stealthily behind the shed. I felt so guilty. A strange tingle of excitement floated through me as I opened the packet, took out a Bonio and took my first ever bite. It was delicious! Sinking my teeth into the crunchy biscuit was bliss, and before I knew it I had eaten the whole packet. I remember Charlie's big sad eyes looking up at me, wondering why he wasn't getting any biscuits.

'It wasn't long before I was hooked on them. My mother thought that the reason she was buying four packets of Bonios a week, instead of the usual one, was due to Charlie's growing appetite. Little did she know that her seven-year-old daughter had been transformed into a "Biccie Junkie", and could be seen behind the garden shed every evening, eating her heart out while an emaciated, straggly labrador looked up at her.'

'Are you okay?' Bill interrupted. 'Do you want to carry on?'

'It's okay,' I assured him. 'I have to do this. From

then on, even during my teenage years, I continued to mess around with dog biscuits.'

'What did you take?' a member of the group asked.

'Oh, anything really. I tried all the brands – Winalot, Sam, Pedigree Chum. I think the best one was the Chum. Then I tried the hard stuff one day – dog food!'

'Ohhh,' the group gasped in horror.

'Never again!' I added.

'Aaah,' sighed everybody in relief.

'It wasn't bad though,' I defended. 'Mainly it was because of my cats that I had to give it up. Like me, they were quite fond of dogfood. If I ever left a tin on the table they would jump up, stick in their heads and fish around for leftovers. Sometimes they would get their heads stuck in the tin, fall off the table and walk around the kitchen with the tins still stuck on

their heads. It was chaos! Dog food was a no-no!'

Suddenly I stalled. Telling my story was becoming increasingly difficult. But I had come this far already, and it would be weak and show a lack of determination on my part if I didn't go on now.

My voice was shaky but somehow I managed to continue. 'I ... I got a job ... in a chicken-slaughter factory. My part was putting the chickens on the conveyor belt. It was a case of "Now you see it, now you don't". One minute I could see their heads bobbing up and down in terror, the next minute, after they got the chop, I could see their legs bobbing up and down. At night, I used to have terrible nightmares. A big headless chicken would pick me up off my bed and place me on the conveyor belt. But instead of getting my head chopped off I emerged on the other side looking like an overfertilised Bonio. It was awful, but it was then that Frank came.'

Everyone in the class sat up, listening eagerly.

'It was love at first sight – sort of. Frank's looks had nothing to do with it – he had none! His teeth were all over the place, major orthodontic work was needed, and he had some annoying habits, for example blowing his nose until I was sure that his sinuses were going to pop out. But still I loved him. He was the only butcher I knew who wrote poetry. Once he even tried his hand at alliteration.

'"What d'ya think of this?" he asked me one day.

> *"The little lazy lump of lard laughed,*
> *Nobody will save you, sir!*
> *Save me, save me, Sarah*
> *Screamed Stanley stating something stupid."*

'He was a genius! I loved the "Save me, save me, Sarah" bit – it really blended in nicely with the screams of the chickens in the background.

'Frank could handle any situation. Once, my father invited myself and Frank up to his house. One of his cows had a bladder problem, and when we arrived the vet was just leaving. We entered the kitchen and Frank made a bee-line for the whiskey bottle on the table. He took a great slug of it and while he was doing so, my father just scratched his head and watched him, trans-fixed. "What's he doing drinking the cow's urine sam-ple?" he asked me.

'How Frank managed just to say politely, "Oh, I was wondering what that strange taste was", and quietly excuse himself to go to the bathroom was beyond me. Oh, but sure, he was a great man!

'With Frank now in my life, my habit seemed to have ceased. But it hadn't. Gradually the longing for a sweet Bonio came back to haunt me. I couldn't resist the temptation, and eventually I succumbed to the dog biscuits again. Suddenly my life started to fall apart. In a state of panic I tried to go cold turkey but I just couldn't do it. After a couple of months, Frank started to suspect that something was wrong. My whole personal-ity had changed and I didn't return his calls. When he came to my house one day and found me sitting on the floor eating dog biscuits, he was utterly disgusted. The house was like a pigsty, crumbs all over the place.

'Frank issued me an ultimatum – him or the Bonios. He shoved a biscuit under my nose to see if I would take it. When I snatched it from him and told him to get out, he knew that I was beyond control. He left then. That was the last time I ever saw him.'

Silence. Everything was quiet. The ticking of a clock could be heard. It was eight o'clock. I looked at the group. Some had been emotional, others were sniffling. This was either an allergic reaction to my perfume or else they were actually moved by my story.

'Please finish,' said Bill, wiping a tear away.

'That was about a year ago now. I have to say that Frank's departure really shook me up. I realised that I had to try and pull myself together before it was too late. That's why I'm here today. I can finally admit that I need help. I have only ever had two great loves of my life – dog biscuits and Frank. I've lost one and I certainly don't want the other. I need to kick the habit. Can you help me?' I pleaded, a big tear rolling down my cheek.

Suddenly everyone stood up and started to clap. Bill came over and hugged me and said that they would do everything they could to help me. He said that I was the bravest woman he had ever met. Hearing this I smiled and at that moment I thought I saw, just for a second, the ghost of my old dog Charlie wagging his tail and a box of Bonios by his side. When I saw this, I knew that it would be a very long time before I ever ate a Bonio again. I was saved.

Past the Moon

A N D R E W   T O F T

He lay there, his thoughts naked, listening to the wind as it hummed through the drain outside.

> *'Now I lay me down to sleep,*
> *I pray to God my soul to keep,*
> *And if I die before I wake,*
> *I pray to God my soul to take.'*

A stillness swooped inside him and pronounced a lonely space heavy with emptiness. A light crept through the window and lit up a corner of the room. His books were loose on the ground. His father would not like this. He would be mad.

The boy jumped out of bed and tidied them up as quickly as he could. Then he got back into bed and lay there relieved, staring at the light in the corner. Suddenly it disappeared. He pulled the curtain from the ledge and looked outside. The moon lay motionless. It was bright except for a dark grey mist that hung over it. It seemed so alone, so distant from any neighbouring star.

A sudden slam stopped his thoughts and he knew *he* was home. The silence was deafening. Fear lunged itself into his thoughts. Since his mother had died it had been like this. He loved her and needed her now more than ever. He waited, too frightened to breathe. A mist filled his eyes. He tried to sleep, but it was impossible. Then he heard the menacing steps as they barged clumsily down the hall. The door opened. The light went on. He sat up straight, trying to focus. A blur blocked the sight of him.

'Why isn't the front room clean?'

'You only asked me to clean the kitchen,' the boy replied.

'Don't you dare answer me back, boy. Now, get up and get my dinner.'

The boy rose quickly and cautiously made his way past him. He raised his hand. The boy did not dare protect himself. The man flaked his hand down upon bare skin. A searing pain tore through the boy's body. He hurried up the hall with his head drooped, shielding the tears from *his* view. *He* hated crybabies.

The chips took a while to heat up. All the time the father stared at him. The boy did not dare to turn around. Catching his eye would be dangerous and he did not want to prolong the torture. He was cold now. He could feel the tingle of chill repeat itself as it pulsated through his veins. A small grey spider came up from the side of the cooker and began scampering across the counter. The boy sensed the cruel, narrow brown eyes staring at his back. Then suddenly he was pushed aside and a hand slammed down on the spider.

The chips were ready now and the boy went to the freezer to get the sausages. The man hovered around, probing him into making a mistake. He liked to hit the boy. He thrived on it. The boy hated him. It had become a psychological battle. How could the boy defeat him? The father had hurt him more with those slaps than he had understood. He had picked at the boy's mind and turned it into a block of fear and frustration. The outcome was inevitable.

While pouring the beer, the boy spilled some on his father's leg.

'You're useless,' the man began. 'I'm going to teach you a lesson you'll never forget.' He picked up a belt. 'If you think I am strict you should have lived in my house when I was your age.'

With these words he gave the first whack. The pain was eased by the numbness from the cold. A second lash severed the skin. A drop of blood fell from the boy's back and formed itself neatly in a crack on the floor. The third strike was the most painful. It ripped through the boy's body, cutting every restraint in him and causing him to scream aloud. A steady trickle of blood began to stream from his back.

His father handed him a rag and told him to return to his room and not to show his face in the morning. The boy's tears were so strong they blinded him. What he really needed now was some sympathy and a gentle hug, but he knew this would happen only if he went past the moon and past the stars and if he ...

'Go!' *he* shouted.

A Narrow Escape

ALICE STACK

'Come on, Blackie,' called Jean. 'Time for your bath.'

Oh no, not this again. Speedy raced off the tell the other clans, and the rest of us hurried to our positions on Blackie's head.

It probably sounds strange to you, but this is a real emergency. If we don't make it up there in time we will all be drowned. Bath time can be disaster time if you happen to be a flea like us. If you hear the call you evacuate right away and Speedy always tries to get to any clan that doesn't hear. That lot on the back leg are a bit deaf. I do hope that they and Speedy get up in time.

On my way up I fell into step with Ivy. Now Ivy is always hungry and she tended to annoy Blackie more than the rest of us. She was lamenting the fact that she was having to give up her home.

'But you have to move every time our Blackie has a bath, so why are you so upset this time?' I said, hoping that this might comfort her.

'I know, I know. But this place was so lovely and dry and warm,' she wailed. I walked on, for I knew that I would only upset her even more if I continued talking.

Well, I think we all made it okay, and after his bath

when Blackie settled down to his dinner we all relaxed and helped ourselves to a bite or two of supper as well. Little did we know then that something even more dangerous than bath time was about to occur.

Blackie finished eating and was let outside to run around for a while before bedtime. He loved to get out, and was especially happy this time because he could hear a couple of his friends howling and barking in the distance. I could sense that he longed to go and join them. There was a shout from the house – it was Jean telling Blackie to get to his bed. Blackie turned but noticed that Jean wasn't paying too much attention to him. He waited for a while and when the second call failed to come he silently padded off down the lane. We were scared. Blackie had never disobeyed his owners before. Then we heard the barking again. 'They must be calling him,' whispered Ivy. I nodded.

There were five dogs altogether, and there was much excitement when Blackie arrived. I'd never seen such running about and yapping and I had the feeling that this gang was going to get up to something. Under fences they went, through a few hedges and then – oh no! – there were sheep everywhere, running about in all directions, bleating and jumping as they tried to get away from the dogs. Even I know that if a dog kills a sheep he will be shot – surely Blackie knows that too. If Blackie gets killed, then there is no way out for us flees either. But we were helpless.

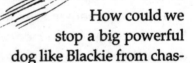

How could we stop a big powerful dog like Blackie from chasing the sheep? We just had to hold on and hope that Blackie would go home. Speedy had seen that two sheep were down and that the other dogs were hovering over a third. Blackie seemed to be slowing down and hanging back a bit. This was all new to him, but the others looked as though they had done it before and were enjoying the hunt.

Blackie had stopped now and was just watching. He was trying to understand why the other dogs were chasing the sheep until they fell down. He was puzzled and worried and we could sense it. After what seemed like a long time he backed away, turned and ran home.

In the morning the kitchen was a hive of activity. The phone was ringing. Some of the neighbours were in and I kind of felt that it was all connected to what we had seen last night – Blackie, the sheep, the chase. I couldn't see people's faces nor could I follow all the talk. But the dead sheep were mentioned, and I heard Blackie's name and the shot gun was pointed to once or twice.

Please look innocent, Blackie, I thought to myself. I know that you were with the pack and that you were even enjoying it for a while. But you didn't kill. I know that you didn't kill.

Meanwhile, Ivy was jumping up and down and wanting her breakfast. 'Not now, Ivy, this is not the time to bite. Poor Blackie is trying his best to look calm and quiet. All our lives are at stake here. Please don't annoy him just now.' I was pleading with her through my teeth. And I could feel such tension in the air. Had they noticed that Blackie was out last night? Surely they don't think that he could kill. If they knew that he was running with the pack ... my mind was racing. Just then I noticed that Jean was down and petting Blackie and that the kitchen was quiet again. 'Poor old boy,' she said. 'You didn't do anything. I told the farmers so.'

The relief ran through me like a wave. And I think I almost heard a cheer from that clan down there on the back leg. Even they realised that we had all had a very narrow escape.

The Suppression of Emotion

MARY SMITHWICK

She trudged wearily home from the supermarket, weighed down by the shopping bags, full of ordinary, everyday things. She had nearly picked up a bag of nappies today, and put them in the trolley. Such a silly little thing, but it brought it all flooding back. The gentle sun of the calm winter's day had brought mothers out in their droves, pushing buggies gurgling with life. It wasn't fair, she thought bitterly. Why not them? Why take her sweet little baby, and leave theirs? She had loved hers just as much, with her round blue eyes, her little button nose, and her masses of fair downy hair. She could still remember the sweet smell of her, the delicious smell of little babies. Memories haunted her everywhere, but she still hadn't shed a tear. That would have been giving in to the unfairness of the world, accepting it. So she kept her feelings in, and kept up a hard cold façade in front of her emotions.

* * *

The little girl shuffled miserably out into the playground for lunchtime. It had been a beautiful morning but now the day had turned nasty. She knew it couldn't last, just like the way their happiness over the little baby couldn't last. A tear trickled down her pale little cheek, sharp and salty. Sometimes she wished she could just talk to her mother about it, ask her why; just hug her and be embraced in her loving arms, and have all her sadness washed away like before. But Mummy never hugged her anymore. A second tear chased the first one down her cheek at the thought of this. Sometimes she thought Mummy felt the baby had been taken away because they had all loved her so much, and now, if she ever loved anyone again, they'd be taken away too. She wished she could tell Daddy this, but he always seemed so preoccupied with something. She wished ... she wished ... she wished she could get the picture of the little white coffin out of her head, blurred by the tears she and Daddy had shed, and those Mummy hadn't. She wished home could be like it was before ...

* * *

Trudging home, under grey skies full of the fury of a storm to come, he had time to think. With his briefcase tucked neatly underneath his arm and his smart coat tied, he looked businesslike, dependable. But he knew himself it was only a front, put up to hide the turmoil of emotions underneath. He was sick of being dependable and capable. He was sick of having to continue on as if it were all long past, sick of being the 'strong man'. He thought of his wife at home, so cold, so distant, yet he could see underneath all that, he could see the intense pain she was suffering. He thought of his little daughter, always so sad and solemn now, never a smile leaping to her face and making dimples in her cheeks. He thought of his other little daughter, whom they had only known for such a short time – oh, such a short, short time – but who had left a gaping hole in all their lives. He thought of the earth raining down on the spotless, white coffin, soon covering it totally. It seemed so barbaric, doing that to a little baby. But ... he kept on walking.

It was dark when he arrived home, and the curtains were pulled. He wiped his feet on the mat, and left his briefcase in the hall. He realised how these little rituals were all that was left of their once perfect family life. His wife was sitting as usual, staring vacantly at the TV screen. His daughter came down the stairs, frowning, as if thinking that bad as it was to be on her own upstairs, it could only be worse down here. A wave of anger swept over him. He was losing his wife, and their daughter was going to grow up without decent parents! It couldn't go on. He took a deep breath and switched off the television.

'We have to talk ...'

The First Day I Went to the Canal

A N N E - M A R I E   C U S A C K

All the boats were docked. The water was high. There
were bridges on either side of me. The railings were
green with trees around them. On the other side of the
railings it was slippery. The sun was shining on the
water and the water looked yellow. There was a man-
made waterfall and I could hear the sound of it. It was
all quiet and peaceful. I liked it there.

Seariders

IONIA NÍ CHRÓINÍN

When the murky waters run cold,
The Seariders' secrets unfold.
Pure white horses scream their words,
Leering faces draw their swords.

With one sweep of their arm
They slash at the waves,
Sending icy cold water
Splashing into the caves.

Then facing each other,
Their helmets closed down,
They raise up their swords,
Each one with a frown.

Cries ring out
As their enemy is slain,
Some of pride,
And some of pain.

Horses fall down
With a sigh of distress,
Only heads to be seen,
Like figures in chess.

And suddenly then,
At the first light of dawn,
The horses stop screaming,
The riders go numb.

They collapse in the water,
With no voice to wail,
They try to start swimming,
But with every stroke fail,

Then they slowly start sinking,
Down under the pool,
And cool fresh water,
Will once again rule.

My Mother's
Childhood Memories of Christmas

DEIRDRE HAYES

One night we got tired of watching TV so we turned it off. My mother had just finished the washing up and sat down. We started telling stories, and at last it was my mother's turn. She thought for a while and then started to tell us about her childhood memories of Christmas on Bere Island. We were all fascinated by what she was telling us.

With only one shop in the little village the excitement of all the children the night the shop owner decorated the windows and put the toys out on display was unbelievable. All the little noses glued to the glass, picking out the toy that they wanted and hoping that Santa would bring it.

When they got their school holidays the next day, the Christmas preparations really got going. The first job was to cut down a nice Christmas tree from the farm and to get berried holly to decorate the windows and pictures in the house.

My grandfather had the job of making the crib in the small village church. So my mother and her younger sisters gathered ivy and hay for him from the farm to put around the crib.

Another busy day was set aside to kill the fowl to give away as gifts to relations in Bishopstown in Cork city. The children were very unhappy having to go out to get the chickens, so they pretended that the chickens had run away to a nearby farm and that they couldn't find them. Their father did not believe them of course, because he knew they had pet names for the chickens and that they loved them and told these fibs every year. Sad faces were seen all that day and nobody spoke to the father because he was blamed for killing their pets.

The day after, their mother got the boat to Castletownbere to go shopping in Patrick's Street in Cork city.

Another night they would all sit around the table writing cards to friends and relations. Letters and parcels were made up and posted too. When all of that was out of the way the children started to decorate the house. A big bunch of holly was tied to the front door and streamers were hung across the ceiling of the living room and the hall. Sprigs of holly were put in the windows and over the pictures. The tree was decorated with fairy-lights and bells.

The next day the shopping had to be done. Vegetables were brought in from the farm and a big tree was cut into blocks for the fire. The Christmas pudding was boiled and made ready for Christmas Day.

At last it was Christmas Eve. Their mother made mince pies, cooked the ham and prepared the turkey. Sand was put into empty jamjars, and small white candles were placed in the jars and lit in every window

of the house. One big red Christmas candle was lit by the youngest child in the house and placed in the middle of the kitchen table. When teatime came they all sat around the table and a big barmbrack was cut and Christmas cake too.

Excitement was starting to build up for the young children as they hung the Christmas stockings on the mantelpiece. For once they went off to bed without having to be told. They looked out the window first at all the twinkling lights from the little thatched houses in the next townland and also to see if Santa was on his way. Their father had filled a bag of hay and hung it on a post for the reindeer. He had also given the cows an extra bit of hay because it was a special night for them too.

At last it was Christmas morning. All the children got up early to see the little gifts Santa had brought and to go to first Mass. They did not get very expensive toys but they were still happy. They usually got pencils, reading books, school bags, colouring books and apples and oranges. They played for about a half an hour with their toys and then got ready to go to Mass while their Mother put the stuffing in the turkey.

The whole family went to Mass together, exchanging Christmas greetings with their friends and neighbours on the way. My Mother and her sisters sang in the choir with their class. While they sang the beautiful hymns the true meaning of Christmas really came to them.

When they got home, they all sat down to enjoy their breakfast together. Then gifts were opened and everyone was very happy. Neighbours called in with gifts and to wish everybody a happy Christmas.

The turkey was put in the oven and the dinner was prepared. The young children were busy playing with their toys. Their father got a big fire going and the atmosphere of Christmas was all around.

At last the dinner was ready and all eyes were on the turkey, waiting for their father to carve it up. After eating a beautiful dinner the lights were turned off, brandy was poured over the Christmas pudding, and it was lit and carried to the table in a blaze of light. There was a big cheer when the children saw this, and they thanked their mother for the wonderful meal she had put before them.

Their mother was told to sit back and relax by the log fire while the girls tidied up and washed the ware, and she was given her Christmas presents then.

As my mother was coming to the end of her story we all begged her to bring us down to Bere Island and to have a beautiful Christmas just as she did when she was a child.

The Gambler

RAMI OKASHA

Fourteen, but very mature.
Fag in hand, he'll give
You the lowdown on the
Slot machines, as he pours
Money in.

You are only up to his shoulder
As he sits on the bar-stool.
'How's the German fellas goin'?'
He'll aimlessly inquire.
'Fierce good stuff, German,'
As he shoots a few cops,
And swerves a bollard.

'I was in Rome last month,'
He'll tell you by way of
Conversation, as he lights up.
'Fabulous. Absolutely Fabulous.'
He deftly avoids plummeting over a cliff.
'With a mate, you know.'

'Thinking of taking it up, y'know.'
He takes a drag.
'Italian. Fabulous place.'

He tosses the butt on
The ground. Glowing.
You can see his stained teeth
Glow in the dim light.
The smell of stale smoke
Invades your nostrils.

'Listen, I see ya around, boy.'
He's right. You are a boy.
He curtails:
'G'is a buzz sometime,'
And saunters off to the quasar.

Best fella around, if only he'd
Start again.

The Winter's Sleep

KAREN ROCHFORD

The night is long
But fur is deep,
You will be warm
In winter's sleep.

The food is gone
But dreams are sweet,
And they will be
Your winter's meat.

The cave is dark
But dreams are bright,
And they will serve
As winter light.

Sleep my little cubs, sleep.

A Day in the Life of a Full Stop

P E T E R   C A L L A N A N

I am a full stop who has been conceived but not yet born. I wait patiently in the cerebrum where I was conceived, knowing not the day nor the hour when I will be called to my specialist work.

Today my master, Brother Secundus, will start his eighth sentence of the Book of Kells. His eye for minute detail is superb. He is a master at his work. I know that when Secundus calls upon my services I will be painted on only the best vellum, and my surroundings on the page will shine because of its beauty. As Secundus rises, his mind agile and alert, not only does he think of Prime (his morning prayers), but also of his day's labour in the scriptorium. Although his work is painfully tiring, he finds great contentment in seeing the finished product. He enters the chapel and proceeds to his chair where he prays, dedicating his work to God. After breakfast, Secundus advances to the scriptorium where his implements, a few goose quills, lie stacked on a rack. Making himself as comfortable as possible, he begins to write.

Between the illustrations, he writes his beautifully scribed letters which would attract anyone. Once or twice Secundus prepares me for work, but I am not yet called upon to do my duty. I marvel at the falcons he has painted, their wings aching with beauty, or the cat, sleek and thin as the very vellum it is drawn on. It has taken Secundus thirty-five minutes to complete an 'R', but the 'R' is full of grace.

As he works, I daydream of last week, when the barbarous Vikings came and plundered our beautiful monastery. Secundus was writing when the bell rang abruptly, a sure sign of Vikings. Secundus gathered the tools of his trade, and hastily closed the book, but not without making sure that the page would not be smudged. Making his way to the round tower, he climbed the ladder and ascended the stairs. When the entire community was safely installed in the tower, the ladder was raised and, though safe, they nervously watched the advancing Vikings. They came looking for gold and valuable objects, and when they found none they plundered and pillaged the monastery, leaving few buildings intact. When we were sure they had gone we slowly descended from our perch, to find all non-stone buildings destroyed and all farm animals either dead or missing. I will always remember the tears in Secundus's eyes.

But today this shall not happen. The work will be undisturbed. Secundus is thinking of the importance of a full stop: how a sentence can't make sense without one. Since we have started, Secundus has turned the insipid page into a thing of beauty, using only his creative mind and a quill. He thinks how kind God was to give him a talent such as this.

After all of his work this morning, Secundus is

hungry and needs a break, so he goes to the kitchen for a small snack. Being a book-writer, Secundus has the special privilege of eating when he likes, within reason. Coincidentally, the other monks are entering for their lunch after a morning's work in the fields. Secundus, a man of few words, is constantly thinking about his book. He wonders how long it will be before he needs a full stop, and whether he can improve on any part of his book. After more prayers, it is Secundus's turn to work in the fields; this is the least popular shift, for the sun is searing down from twelve to three. While working, Secundus sees two ladybirds scuttling around on a leaf. This gives him an idea for the manuscript. An illustration would be nice, he thinks. At three o'clock, Secundus is given permission to return to the scriptorium. I am feeling tired just from watching Secundus doing such laborious work.

Secundus wishes to colour in his ladybird illustration, and this is done using metal ores. For example, green comes from copper and red from lead. Nearing completion of his eighth sentence as dusk approaches, Secundus wonders if it is time for me, the full stop. No, not just yet. A couple more illustrations before he needs me. But Secundus has time for only two more illustrations, and so I will have to remain in the womb of Secundus's mind for at least another day. Still, I, the full stop, can rest easy because I know that without me the book cannot be finished.

Quiet as Mice

ANNE-MARIE BARRY

I went babysitting to a big posh house,
I was told the child was as quiet as a mouse.
I walked through the door, then 'Ouch, my hair!'
How I wished I wasn't there.

Someone called my name, and voices said, 'Who?'
I looked around, 'No, not another two!'
She said, 'Oh, I forgot to tell you,
You'll have to mind an extra two.'

The lady said, 'I'm off now, kids, be nice,'
And looking at me, 'They're as quiet as mice.'
The door was closed, this was going to be hell,
No sooner said than I heard a yell.

I ran into the kitchen but it was too late,
Two china cups and a china plate
Lay smashed on the floor. I said 'That's that,
I'm going to strangle each little brat.'

I stamped my foot upon the floor,
And screamed aloud, 'I'll come here no more.'
They were so, so noisy, it got to my head,
I said, 'That's it, you're going to bed.'

The lady returned, and said, 'How nice,
And how were the children?''Oh, quiet as mice.'
She asked 'Are you sure?' and I said, 'Not a squeak.'
'Oh good,' she replied, 'come again next week!'

Seagull's First Flight

SARAH   HICKEY

I just can't get him to fly. Every day he sits on the rocks waiting for me to bring him food. Well, today I'm not. If he wants to eat he can go and get something himself. I'm sick of it, all his brothers are up and away, but oh no, not him. The problem is he has no courage, he's scared of heights.

But guess what, I'm going to play a little trick on him. Right, here he comes. I have a fish and I am just going to sit here, on the edge of this ledge. There, I knew it, he's screaming at me to come closer because he's too lazy to come and get it himself. Well, I'm not.

Here he comes and he's trying to get the fish. I step back off the ledge and flap my wings. He thinks I'm still on the ledge and lunges for the fish. He's just fallen and looks slightly sick. I'd better go down and make sure he discovers his wings. Ah, he has. Now I feel pleased. My little son is swooping up and down. My son is flying, actually flying. I think I shall take him down to the water. He hasn't had any food for at least a day.

Well, here we are down at the rocks with the swirling sea before us. He is a bit afraid of the water but he'll get used to it. He sees a fish and is going to get it. He sits on the water and finds it very cold. Then the fish ducks underwater and he goes too. In a minute he pops up with a nice juicy mackerel in his beak. We share it together on a rock.

When the meal is over he swoops up into the sky with me after him. We twist and turn and tumble until the sun goes down. Then we go back home to the little ledge. We sit and watch a fantastic sunset and I think of my little boy.

Bart Simpson

SÉAMUS DE NAIS

Is mise Bart Simpson, cladhaire ceart,
i gcónaí i dtrioblóid má ghlacaim páirt.
Ní páiste mór mé caithfidh mé a admháil
ach más agatsa atá fadhb, táim ar fáil!

Seo iad mo dhintiúirí a Dhude a chroí,
is réabhlóidí ceart mé lán de spraoi.
Ní bheidh mo leithéidse le feiceáil arís,
mar is Rambo óg mise in éadan an dlí!

Bhí troid sa scoil cúpla lá ó shin,
cuireadh páiste bun os cionn sa bhruscairín.
'Bart Simpson chuig an oifig!' a chuala gach n-aon,
mar bhí a fhios ag an máistir go ndearna mé é.

'Simpson, a chladhaire, bailigh leat as an scoil!'
'Tá an ceart agat, a mháistir, caithfidh mé dul!'
'Ach abair liom, Simpson, an bhfuil tú faoi bhrón?'
'Hé, Dude,' arsa mise, 'póg mo thóin!'

Ar aghaidh liom abhaile lán de ghreann,
is i gclós an tí bhí Homer ann,
Bhí comharsa bhéal dorais ag gáire is ag maíomh.
Chuaigh mé suas staighre is fuair mé mo chlaíomh.

Dúirt Homer liom go raibh sé ar buile,
dúirt mé leis, 'Ní bheidh tú a thuilleadh!'
Chaith mé an claíomh suas san aer,
is nuair a tháinig sé anuas bhuail sé é!

Bhí fearg ar Homer is léim sé thar claí,
bhí eagla ar an chomharsa is thosaigh sé ag guí,
'Ó, a Dhia sna Flaithis, tá Homer ag teacht,
le cúnamh Dé coimeád é faoi smacht!'

Bhí Homer réidh chun é a mharú,
Ach tháinig Marge amach le tlú,
'Tar amach díreach, a Homer,' ar sí
'nó is tusa a bheidh ar do ghlúine ag guí!'

'Ceart go leor, Marge, ná téigh thar fóir.
is é do mhac BART a thosaigh an gleo.'
Leis sin do rug sí greim ar mo chluas,
is tharraing sí isteach sa teach mé ar luas.

Mhínigh mé dóibh cad a tharla ar scoil,
is thosaigh sí féin agus Homer ag gol.
Anois tá orm an dán seo a scríobh,
nó gheobhaidh mé rud níos measa ná claíomh!!!

My Winter

BRENDAN JACKSON

If I could see myself now,
I would see a tree, through spectacles.
A tree with browning leaves about to fall.
After its summer months of glory,
Wishing it was summer still,
And not winter rain and coldness.

A tree that has been forced out of bloom into bareness,
Stripped of its vitality.
Every autumn I am stripped
And am forced to put on my spectacles
To look for something I don't want –
School is my winter.

History

MARY SMITHWICK

'You're history, man,' the rough voice barked, as Denis fell, a strong arm shoving him backwards. He met the rough stone wall with a thump, painfully grazing the back of his head. Then the group advanced menacingly, buffeting him about like a piece of flotsam on a stormy sea. He whimpered, but didn't try to escape. He knew that if he ran, they would catch him. They always did.

A teacher approached, lumbering over from the other side of the playground like a ship, bobbing from side to side. He pulled his chalk-covered cloak around him, as if to summon up some vestige of authority.

'Anything the matter, boys?' he muttered, peering short-sightedly over his glasses at them. The group closed around Denis, swallowing him up. The sea of bodies tensed, a silent reminder that it was futile to make any protest.

'No, sir,' they chorused. One or two sniggered.

'Very good, very good,' he twittered, seeing only a crowd of boys in front of him. True, that young fella there looked a bit dishevelled, he thought, but didn't he always? What was his name again? Darren? Derek? Denis? He never could seem to remember his name.

He was one of those quiet lads who just seemed to fade into the background, as if he didn't want you to notice him.

'Well, see it stays that way, and, em, play nicely together.'

'Yes, sir,' they chorused. More giggles. He lumbered off, and they turned back to Denis.

That afternoon in class, Denis was in trouble once more.

'What do you mean, you've lost your homework again?' the teacher exclaimed, exasperated. 'How can you be so careless?' Denis mumbled some half-hearted apology and the teacher sighed, looking at the trembling lips and round, lonely eyes. He couldn't understand it, he had been such an enthusiastic boy before, always eager. Strange, that ...

'Now, is there anyone else?' he snapped. Denis shifted uncomfortably in his seat. Of course he was, as usual, on his own. But he'd got used to it, really he had. He didn't mind. Honestly, he didn't! You could get used to anything, he had found. You could get used to spending lunchtime on your own, to not getting all the nice bits of your lunch, to always being left out ...

He trudged home slowly, kicking up the leaves with boots almost as heavy as his head. It was better going home on your own, though. No one to pounce on you like a cat, no unfriendly smiles, no mocking laughs. Anger boiled up inside him. It wasn't fair! Why did they pick on him? He wasn't any different to them.

'Teacher's pet!' they'd taunt him, pushing him from side to side.

'Mummy's boy!' they jeered and chanted. He hated them! Hated them! Hated them! He kicked a little bin in frustration, then looked around to check had anyone been watching him. The anger died down inside him. What was the point? Rain began to drop slowly down, and he hurried home.

His father had often told him to simply hit back. 'Thump 'em – hard,' he'd say impatiently, wondering why his son was so soft.

But it was no good. They could always hit back harder, just like they could always run faster. Anyway, it wasn't so much the physical bullying he minded, it was the continual mental torment. They said such horrible things – could they really mean them? And there was no point trying to say something back, they always thought of something meaner, something more hurtful. They were right, he was just stupid!

The months and weeks crawled by, one continuous prison spell. Then one day, Denis didn't come to school any more. No one knew what had happened, and no one really cared. Maybe he had moved away, or changed schools, or ... who knows? His teacher was relieved that he no longer had to deal with him, and the crowd found someone else to supply homework and lunch. Someone else filled his solitary desk, some-one else cried bitter tears, had their lunch taken, 'lost' their homework. There would always be someone else. Someone else to be 'history'.

My Nanny

LISA CARTHY

My Nanny's name is Ann. She has brown hair and brown eyes. Before my Nanny got married she was a Doyle. Nanny used to live in Kilkaven, Wellington-bridge. Now Nanny is married to a man called Aidan Carthy. We call him Grandad. Nanny now lives in Ballyfrom, Duncormick, Co. Wexford.

Sometimes Nanny is very funny. She is very small and good-looking for her age. The size of shoes Nanny takes is a size six. The cigarettes she smokes are called Benson and Hedges. Her favourite perfume is Lulu and she loves the smell of it. She also loves Dairy Milk chocolates.

Nanny has seven sisters and three brothers. She has seven children of her own. Three of her children are living in England and four are living in the area. She has three grandchildren.

For Easter, Nanny goes to England to see her children. When she is on a boat and the sea is rough Nanny sometimes gets white in the face. She hates travelling on boats.

Every Christmas she bakes over fifteen Christmas puddings and as many as five Christmas cakes. Nan gives great Christmas presents. Last year she gave me

fifty
pounds
and this year she gave
me a pair of black Wrangler
jeans and a padded shirt. Nan is very nice to me. She
lets me sleep whenever I want to.

You're the best Nan, I love you.

Shattered

C A T H Y   T O F T

The picture was crumpled. All four corners were dog-eared. The frame was broken, the glass shattered. In my desperate attempt to get the picture out I had damaged both the glass and frame. All the people in the picture were smiling. Six people grouped together beside a big oak tree. A father, mother and four children. A big happy family, almost as solid as the tree itself.

It used to stand on the fireplace. It was always gleaming and shining. Even when kids rampaged from room to room, the mess piled up and the walls seemed to be coming down around us, it stood there, perfect. Almost as perfect as the family. Now the picture lay shattered in my hand. Just as the family was.

It was a clear summer's day. The sun smiled in a blue sky. It wasn't raining and wet and windy with angry lightning and groaning thunder, the way it should be. People weren't wearing all black and grouped together around the graveside. They were wearing coloured clothes, some even white. I thought Andy, Mark and John would look out of place in their suits of dark grey, blue and green. But it was I who looked out of place in my black dress and shoes.

I couldn't go to the church. How could I when I didn't believe in God? Fifteen years of faith had disappeared in one night. But I had to see the coffin being lowered. I had to see that she was gone or I'd never believe it. I still waited for her to come home from work and sit with her feet up watching television but always falling asleep. I waited for her in the morning to drive me to school in her battered yellow mini. I waited for her to help me with my homework, to laugh at my jokes, to wipe away my tears when I cried. All the millions of little things which made up the jigsaw puzzle of my life were gone. The things I had grown up with and taken for granted. And I knew that I would have to carry on waiting.

The coffin was being lowered. Slowly, slowly, ever so slowly. This time I didn't care about the tears. I watched them fall to the ground and seep into the soil. I looked at the people gathered together. I looked at the cars passing outside. I looked at the two blackbirds circling overhead. I looked at everything except the small patch of earth in front of me.

A picture of her came suddenly to me. All I could see was her back, her favourite pink jumper and the knot of her apron. I could smell her perfume. I can never describe that warm, safe feeling that rose up inside me. That's how I'll always remember her. That's why I refused to go to the funeral home and see her body laid out. I want to remember her full of life and not dead and limp.

There were flowers everywhere. Wreaths, bunches, wildflowers, roses, lilies, tulips. They dropped their heads as if in mourning. Their smell lingered in the air for a long time afterwards. I will always remember that smell. It was the scent of death.

It seemed an eternity passed. And yet things carried on as always. People had begun to depart. I wondered what I would do. There was nothing I wanted to do any more. I felt my world had come apart. It had ended at five o'clock on a busy highway street.

People came back to the house afterwards. There were cakes and sausage rolls and sandwiches and tea. It was like a party. I couldn't eat. I found it difficult to talk. The house was full of people and yet so empty without her.

'I hate funerals.' Her voice drifted into my mind. It was so clear she could almost have been beside me. 'When I die I don't want everybody to mourn my death because I will be in heaven.'

Everyone was in the house. The neighbours, people from the town, the butcher, the baker. Mrs Jones, the hotel owner. People flocked in from far and wide. Her brothers and sisters, old school friends, distant relations. They all had a word of praise, a smile, a look of sympathy, an offer of help. Even Mrs Kennedy was there. She had quarelled with Mum in the past. But they had become friends. I heard her say in her loud voice: 'Poor Anna, left to cope with four men in the house.'

How would I cope? My energy had been wiped away with the car crash and shattered into a million different pieces with the picture frame.

It was over. The funeral was over, leaving an empty void inside me. There was nothing left now. Silence enveloped the house like a thick blanket. It was almost suffocating. I escaped to the solace of my room. Every night I cried myself to sleep.

Hours turned slowly into days and days into weeks. Life went on without her. John went back to London, to his job and wife and kids. Mark and Andy went away to college. Dad slowly but surely picked up the pieces of his life and went back to work. He even began to go out in the night time. His face was no longer thin and gaunt; he put on some weight. I was the only one who refused to come out of my shell. Everything took time with me. It was a long time before I went back to school, a long time to go out to buy clothes, to eat my food, to go back to Mass. It was like learning to walk all over again.

It was a year to the day she died that I found the courage to go to her grave. It was a summer's day. Everything was still. I could hear my footsteps on the gravel and the click of the gate as I entered. The grave-yard was small and empty. I reached the grave quickly. It was neat and tidy. There were no longer masses of flowers and freshly dug earth. It was now covered in with marble and even had a small head-stone. The inscription read:

In loving memory of Margaret Catherine Townsend.

I traced the lettering with my finger. Someone had been looking after the grave. It had fresh flowers and a few small ornaments. It didn't look different any more. It blended in with its surroundings. I placed the

huge bunch of smiling sunflowers on her grave. They had always been her favourite flowers. They always reminded me of her. I read the small neat handwriting on the card for the last time: To Mum, I will love you always, Anna.

I was no longer afraid. To my surprise the graveyard was peaceful. There was just one more thing to do.

The picture was ruffled and crumpled and dirty. The frame was different, as was the glass. It stood back on the mantelpiece just as it always had. And even though everything around it had changed, it still remained the same.

Bríd na mBrionglóidí

CAOIMHE NÍ CHOMHRAÍ

Bhí mé ag eitilt. Ba éan mé. Bhí me i dtír i bhfad i gcéin. Bhí ...

'BRÍD!'

Ba bheag ná gur léim mé as mo chraiceann. Bhí an mháistreás ina seasamh os mo chomhair, a lámha ar a corróga aici.

'Sea?' arsa mise ar nós óinsí.

'Ar mhaith leat mo cheist a fhreagairt?' a d'fhiafraigh an mháistreás.

Ní raibh tuairim agam céard é an cheist fiú amháin.

'Um ... 500m,' arsa mise sa deireadh.

'Ba mhaith liom a chur i gcuimhne duit go bhfuil muid ag déanamh Gaeilge, ní Matamaitic,' arsa an mháistreás.

D'éirigh liom éalú uaithi ag a dó dhéag. Thug mé liom mo lón agus shuigh mé ar an mballa á ithe agus ag brionglóidigh.

Ní imrím mórán leis na gasúir ar scoil. Ní maith leo mé, mar nuair a labhraíonn siad liom ní fhreagraím iad, mar bím ag brionglóidigh. Mar sin, ceapann siad go bhfuil mé mór ionam fhéin.

Shuigh mé ar an mballa ag brionglóidigh. Nuair a bhím á dhéanamh seo, ní thugaim mórán faoi deara.

Ach d'airigh mé an ciúnas sa chlós. Bhreathnaigh mé ar m'uaireadóir. Bhí sé a dó a chlog! Bhí an rang imithe isteach sa scoil le huair go leith anuas agus mise fós i mo shuí ar an mballa gan fiú amháin an clog cloiste agam.

Rith mé isteach sa scoil ar nós na gaoithe. D'oscail mé doras an tseomra ranga. Chas an rang iomlán i mo threo. Sheas mé ansin i m'óinseach. Bhí an seomra chomh ciúin go gcloisfeá féar ag fás. Cheap mé go raibh mé sábháilte mar bhí an mháistreás ag scríobh ar an gclár dubh. Thosaigh mé ag siúl i dtreo mo shuíocháin. Ach go tobann lig an mháistreás scread aisti.

'Bríd, céard a cheapann tú atá á dhéanamh agat ag teacht isteach ag an am seo?'

'Um, n-n-níor thug mé f-f-faoi d-deara g-go raibh an r-rang imithe i-i-isteach,' arsa mise go neirbhíseach.

'Ó,' arsa an mháistreás, 'cheapfainn go mbeadh sé sách soiléir go raibh an rang imithe isteach má bhí an clós folamh.'

Thosaigh an rang ag gáire. Las m'aghaidh le náire. Bhreathnaigh an mháistreás an-sásta go raibh sí dom náiriú.

'Suigh síos,' arsa an mháistreás liom.

Ní bhfuair mé aon phionós uaithi. Ní bhacann sí liom

ach nuair is féidir léi mé a náiriú.

Nuair a shroich mé baile, chuaigh mé isteach sa seomra suite. Chaith mé mé fhéin ar an tolg go gruama. Phioc mé suas an páipéar nuachta. Bhreathnaigh mé air. Sa chúinne bhí fógra:

COMÓRTAS

Scríobh scéal samhlaíoch faoi do rogha ábhar.

1ú DUAIS: *Ríomhaire don scoil agus £20 don bhuaiteoir.*

2ú DUAIS: *Ciclipéid don scoil agus £10 don bhuaiteoir.*

Seol do scéal chuig:

Digital, Baile Briota, Gaillimh.

Rith mé suas staighre agus fuair mé páipéar. Ní raibh mórán ama agam cur isteach ar an gcomórtas. Shuigh mé ar chathaoir i mo sheomra agus scríobh mé leathanach i ndiaidh leathanaigh agus sa deireadh bhí scéal scríofa agam faoi ghasúir bhochta a bhí ina gcónaí ar na sráideanna. Ag a haon déag a chlog chuaigh mé chuig an leaba. Thit mé i mo chodladh ag brionglóidigh faoi chéard a tharlódh dá mbuafainn an duais sa chomórtas.

Ar maidin phreab mé as an leaba. Bhí mé ríméadach faoi mo scéal, ach d'airigh mé go raibh rud éigin nach raibh déanta agam. Shiúil mé isteach sa seomra ranga. Ansin tháinig an mháistreás isteach. Dúirt sí le Caitríona na cóipleabhair Matamaitice a bhailiú. Is ansin a bhuail sé mé nach raibh m'obair bhaile déanta agam.

Nuair a tháinig Caitríona chugam dúirt mé nach

raibh an obair déanta agam. Nuair a chuaigh sí suas chuig bord an mhúinteora, chonaic mé go raibh Caitríona ag insint don mháistreás nach raibh an obair bhaile déanta agamsa. D'éirigh an mháistreás dá cathaoir.

'A Bhríd,' a deir sí, 'cén fáth nach bhfuil an obair bhaile déanta agat?'

'Um, bhí mé ag scríobh scéil do chomórtas,' arsa mise léi, agus d'inis mé di faoin gcomórtas. Nuair a bhí mé réidh dúirt sí: 'Tá áthas orm gur maith leat a bheith ag cur do chuid ama amú ag scríobh seafóide.'

Tar éis an lae sin, shocraigh mé nach scríobhfainn scéal do chomórtas riamh arís. Ach cúpla seachtain ina dhiaidh sin, dúradh leis an rang lá amháin dul síos go dtí an halla. Sheas an t-Ardmháistir ar an stáitse. Nuair a bhí gach duine ina shuí dúirt sé: 'Scríobh cailín as an scoil seo scéal do chomórtas. Ba é duais an chomórtais ná fiche punt don scoláire agus ríomhaire don scoil. Tá an-áthas orm a rá gur ghnóthaigh an cailín as ár scoil fhéin an duais. Is í buaiteoir an chomórtais sin ná Bríd Ní Neachtain.'

Ba bheag nár thit mé i laige. D'éirigh liom dul suas ar an stáitse le glacadh le mo fiche punt. Ach an bhfuil a fhios agat céard ab fhearr faoin mbua a fháil sa chomórtas? Aghaidh mo mháistreása! Bhí mé tar éis a thaispeáint di go raibh mé in ann rud éigin a fháil as bheith ag brionglóidigh agus 'ag scríobh seafóide'.

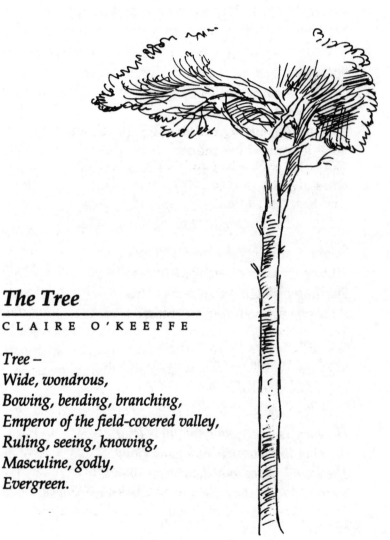

The Tree

CLAIRE O'KEEFFE

Tree –
Wide, wondrous,
Bowing, bending, branching,
Emperor of the field-covered valley,
Ruling, seeing, knowing,
Masculine, godly,
Evergreen.

Song of the Humpbacked Whale

L O I S   W E S T

Splashing, leaping, racing, diving,
Singing, sighing, resting, striving,
Waiting till the end of day,
Then the humpbacked whales will glide away.

Searching, yearning with restless eyes,
While storm-clouds roll over endless skies,
And then with a flick of fin and tail,
It's gone, the song of the humpbacked whale.

Echoing, swelling, soaring, tilting,
Fluting, groaning, strangely lilting;
Swelling through the deep-sea caves,
Pulsating softly, under the waves.

A groan, a wail, a squeak, a whistle,
Floating around like down from a thistle.
Telling of life, of joy, of slaughter,
Flowing through the salty water.

The song is sweet, now soft, now loud,
Blowing like a wisp of billowing cloud,
The sound glides low, then starts to sail,
Then it's gone, the song of the humpbacked whale.

Echoing, swelling, soaring, tilting,
Fluting, groaning, strangely lilting;
Swelling through the deep-sea caves,
Pulsating softly, under the waves.

My Pet

LIAM STEWART

I have a pet rabbit. She lives in a burrow on our bank.
I climb up with food to her every day. I bring lettuce
and cabbage to her. Her friend has a burrow beside
her. I call her Mrs Nibble because I have a
book about a rabbit and her name
is Mrs Nibble. I like my
pet rabbit.

A Day in the Life

BELINDA McKEON

'Aye,' My Grandfather would sigh. 'Aye. Your school days are the best days of your life, Mary.'

As I stand before a classroom of screaming four-year-olds on my first day as Junior Assistant Mistress here in Wyman National School, I have finally come to the sad conclusion that my dear old Grandad was indeed a liar. I suppose this means those fairies never did set up camp at the bottom of his cabbage patch either.

I've always fancied myself as the domineering school mistress, a shining example to all teachers, who would nod in approval as I produced yet another brilliant student. So, when my predecessor as Junior Assistant Mistress emigrated for some unknown reason, leaving the infants at Wyman without a teacher, I jumped at the chance.

But this morning, as Mr Savage, the headmaster, bids me farewell, leaving me at the mercy of twenty-six vengeful-looking tots, I find myself bidding farewell to Ms Domineering Schoolmistress.

As I stand here, watching my new 'workmates' tear their classroom apart, a meek-looking child comes to my side and tugs at my sleeve. She smiles in a manner

that I take to be friendly, revealing a few stumpy teeth, and rather a lot of gaps. Looking down at this angelic-looking child, I realise that I have made a friend. Deciding to ditch the domineering bit, I crouch down to her level, shake her sticky hand and croon, 'And what's your name, little girl?'

The smile disappears. Twenty-five children scream with laughter. The child, face spelling blue murder, lifts a chubby leg in rage. I stand rooted to the spot as

a steel-capped Doc Marten boot makes unfriendly contact with my left shin.

'I'm a boy!' he roars in anger.

'Yes ...' I groan, as I hop around my desk on one leg, in agony, 'yes, I know that – now.'

Laura Ingals Wilder never had this problem in *Little House on the Prairie.*

Nor did she ever take over an hour to call the roll. But, then again, prairie children never held gladiator-style wrestling tournaments on top of the teacher's desk. Sonic the duck wasn't there to distract them from their alphabet either. And I've never known prairie children to carry out cruel experiments involving the school's pet budgie and the VCR.

By the time I have managed to free poor Jack from the labyrinth that is the inside of a video machine, he has lost a considerable amount of feathers and I have lost my entire class.

'You will return to the classroom immediately!' I screech, trying to sound authoritative, as I chase all twenty-six of them around the playground. 'Breaktime is not until eleven o'clock!' Not for another twenty min-utes! Now move it!' A sea of faces stare blankly at me, and for one glorious moment, I appear to have controlled the problem. But it is not to be. The screams, shouts and cries resume, even worse than before, ceasing only when a very dissatisfied Mr Savage stomps out of the building. He advances towards me.

'Miss Francis! What is the meaning of this?' roars the burly old chap, his face purple with rage, his arms waving madly about, as if to inform me that the class

I am in charge of is, at present, racing crazily around the schoolyard.

'Get back to your classroom, PRONTO!' he screams at them, showering me in a cascade of saliva as he does so. In a matter of seconds, myself and my infants are back at base. Savage, having unsuccessfully investigated the matter of the feather-filled VCR, leaves the room, pausing only to cast a withering glance in my direction.

I decide to take advantage of the fact that all of my terror-stricken pupils are sitting quietly in their places. So I delve into my faithful handbag in search of that storybook I remembered to bring with me on leaving home earlier this morning. Or did I? I burrow deeper and deeper into the bag, despairing now, as it becomes clear to me that the storybook is still sitting on the kitchen table, and clear to the children that 'the Savage beast', as I hear one boy call him, has returned to his den.

By the time I have declared mission storybook to be a failure, my pupils, having recovered from their encounter with Mr Savage, have restored the classroom to its original mess. When the breaktime bell rings noisily in my thankful ears, the children spill back out to the playground.

The staff-room is a welcoming sanctuary, away from the noise of the playground, and the tumult of the classroom. It soon becomes clear that all the teachers regard the infants as menaces and as they enquire about their behaviour today, I detect a note of sympathy. I sit there, happily munching my nutritious cheese sandwich, when a sudden thought occurs to me, and I ask: 'Why did the last teacher leave in such a hurry, anyway?' I am answered only by knowing looks exchanged across the table.

Back in the war zone and I am clearing away the half-eaten sandwiches and apple cores strewn around the classroom, when a startling, bloodcurdling cry comes from the direction of the toilets. Dropping my collection of discarded lunch, I dash out of the classroom, almost tripping over several children as I go, and march purposefully into the scene of the crime where I am met by a sea of guilty faces. In the corner, an angel-faced girl (although after this morning's incident, I know better than to fall victim to that) is bawling, her tear-stained face pinched up in anger. She furiously informs me that 'He flushed my dolly down the toilet!' while pointing an accusing finger at a protesting boy standing in the doorway. Having sentenced the offender to spend the rest of the day in the corner, I inspect the damage inflicted upon Dolly. Dolly stares pleadingly up at me from the ravages of the toilet bowl, as her mistress continues to wail and lament. There is nothing for it, I decide grimly, but to take the plunge.

Moments later a very soggy Dolly is happily re-united with her grateful mistress, while the brave heroine – that's me – scrubs her live-saving hands.

To my absolute joy, I soon discover that, due to the reincarnation of Dolly, my class is in awe of me. At last! I savour every remaining moment of the day, scarcely able to believe that I have managed to control these monsters.

Just before the lunchtime bell goes, as I read my attentive class a story, I notice Mr Savage hovering at the door. Marching into the classroom he greets me curtly, then straightens his floral tie, and continues, 'Is everything all right, Miss Francis?'

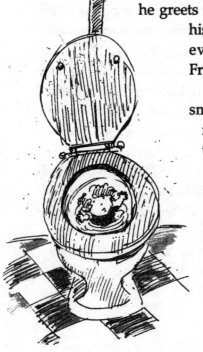

'Why yes, Mr Savage,' I smile, gesturing at my well-mannered class. 'Everything is fine.'

He stares at the children, as though he is unable to believe his eyes. 'I was sure something horrendous had happened,' he declares in his pompous way. 'These children are never quiet for anybody. Except me, of course.' With this, he takes to his heels.

The day goes like a dream until half-past one, when I realise that Tommy, the villain responsible for Dolly's brush with death, is no longer in the corner.

On further inspection, I discover that he is nowhere in the classroom. One of his friends calmly informs me that Tommy, having grown weary of the corner, left for home three hours ago. My astonishment soon turns to horror when I realise that I have no alternative but to report Tommy's sudden departure to Mr Savage.

'What do you mean, he "slipped off home"?' Mr Savage is less than impressed. My knees are knocking. I try to reason with him, but to no avail. I leave Mr Savage's office a quarter of an hour later, after a long lecture on the importance of disciplining young children. By now my apparently 'transformed' class have transformed themselves back into the monsters I faced at nine o'clock this morning.

Tonight I lie in bed reflecting on the first day of my new job. 'Ah well,' I reassure myself. 'It'll be much better tomorrow. New month, new start. Yes, April will be a turning point in my career.' I nod, as I turn out the light.

I sit bolt upright as the awful truth dawns: 'April first!' I wail. 'Oh no – All Fools Day ...'

Best days of your life, eh, Grandad?

Seanchara

MICHELLE LANE

An teach,
Ach 'bean an tí';
'Cén fáth?'
Arsa Seán Ó Laoi.

An pháirc,
Ach 'lár na páirce';
'Ní thuigim é,'
Arsa Liam de Róiste.

An feirmeoir,
Ach 'teach an fheirmeora';
'Níl mé róchinnte,'
Arsa Nóra.

An scoil,
Ach 'mála scoile';
Má bhíonn sé mícheart
Beidh an múinteoir ar buile.

An bhfuil aithne agat
Ar an duine aisteach?
Sin é do sheanchara
An Tuiseal Ginideach.

Hideaway

MICHELLE ALEXANDER

Inside the wardrobe is like a soft cave, filled with the sweet smell of my mother's dresses and the masculine smell of my father's shirts and trousers. I'm hidden totally from sight, with only a streak of light filtering in through a crack. My parents' wardrobe is the best wardrobe to hide in – my brother's and sister's wardrobes are filled with magazines and other rubbish, and you can't sit down. Besides, who wants to hide in a wardrobe full of leather jackets and sweaty shirts? Mum's wardrobe is very big. I can sit down inside it and spread my legs way out, and I still have room to move.

When my eyes grow accustomed to the dark I can see almost everything. I can see my mother's dresses and I can even define the patches in my father's trousers. When I sit down the clothes cover me up and brush against my face. I love the feeling of fabric brushing against my face. It feels like cotton wool, only softer. I'm so well hidden that my mother once came to the wardrobe to get something while I was in it, and she didn't notice me sitting there.

The wardrobe creaks every time I move, and each creak has a different, distinct sound. Sometimes I'm afraid they'll hear the creaking downstairs and find out where my hideaway is, but they never do. I love listening to the cars passing by outside when I'm in the wardrobe. Everything seems so far away – the shouts of laughter, the innocent gossip of neighbours, even the room I'm in seems distant. All that's close to me is the wardrobe and its contents. When I close the wardrobe door I'm in my own world with nobody to intrude. I just sit there and listen and think. Sometimes the fluff from the clothes tickles my nose, which is a nice feeling. Then I sneeze and sneeze.

If I think I'm going to spend a long time in the wardrobe I bring my pillow with me. I lie down and look at the top of the wardrobe. I hardly ever fall asleep though, I just look up and think.

I enjoy listening to people trying to find me when I'm in the wardrobe. Sometimes I'm tempted to answer their calls, but I always manage to restrain myself. I love listening to their confusion and their exclamations of: 'Where could she be? I know she didn't leave the house.' Once or twice I've almost been caught.

When I go into the wardrobe I cease to exist. I am no longer a part of the moving world. I am in a world of my own, a world of imagination where there is no sadness or pain. When I'm in the wardrobe I am no longer an eight-year-old but an adult, all knowing. When I'm in the wardrobe I'm in my own secret hideaway.

A Day in the Life of a Dead Cabbie

LESLIE CARBERRY

*'A dead cabbie's job ain't so bad
(Most of the bad 'uns
Are down the hell way),
Except for havin' to drive Death
Down the Styx Motorway
(when the bypass is coming
I don't know).
But Death, he's always
Swinging his scythe around,
Damaging my cab he is.
Most unruly for
The collector of souls he is.
Now the old Death,
There was a grim reaper
You could trust.
Nice and gothic he was.*

*'Course I miss the wife,
(Still alive you see.)
But, bless her,
Her heart isn't the best.
So here's hoping. Dying!*

'Now there's a funny thing –
Losing your life in a second,
But then all the paper work
To go through with St Peter,
I mean I had to queue
For thirty years.
By the time I got out
Of his office

My wife was in her sixties,
I had grandchildren and
Arnold Flippin' Schwarzenegger
Was President of the US.
Speaking of politics,
Do you see
The Monster Raving Loony Party
Have been re-elected,
Their back-to-rubber-chickens policy
Seems to be workin' out great.

'There is one great thing
About being dead though,
It's that you find out
All the secrets of life.
Like Kennedy for instance,
Wasn't Oswald that shot him,
No, it was some guy
Who just wanted to get
On television
To say he saw everything.
And Elvis,
He's not even dead yet.
He moved to Chigwell and
Became a striptease artist.
Another thing about being dead
Is you meet all the famous people
You'd dream of meeting,
Like Marilyn Monroe,
She's married to George Bush;
And Mother Teresa,
She's become a raver;
And Mr Blobby,
He's a divorce lawyer now.

'So that's about it really,
My route's finished now
So I'm off to the Chant Club,
I just love those Taizé girls.'

Ms McDwyer

CATHY TOFT

It was raining. The rain splashed against the windows with an angry spluttering and tapped on the roof impatiently. Its sound, however, did not deafen the hustle and bustle of the students or the cries in the corridor. Everyone was talking. Everyone, that is, except me. The bitter rain was an all-too-cruel reminder of things to come. The start of a new term. The start of study and homework and books. The start of no more freedom, no going out at night, no lying in bed in the mornings.

Assembly eventually got into order as begrudging students left their friends and news behind and lined up. The chatter died down. Our headmaster had to compete with the rain, and he shouted in the large hall. I did not hear him. I was lost in thought. I was thinking of English class. I dreaded it.

A picture of old Mr Hennessy flashed into my mind. He was big, broad-shouldered and black-haired. He was terrifying. He did not take kindly to misspelled words, unfinished exercises, and texts not learned. He hated work not done, chunks of novels left unread and terrible short stories not studied. His eyes would narrow and glitter dangerously. His mouth would disappear. He spoke softly. He never had to shout. He had done that once years and years ago. It was still talked about.

Assembly was over. I trudged wearily into the class-room and chose a desk at the back, near the windows. I sat alone. I did not really know anyone well in my English class. I watched students talk and laugh about holidays, boys punch each other playfully, and out of the corner of my eye I saw Adam smiling at Sarah. I wished his brown gaze was turned in my direction.

There was a hush as a woman entered the room. She was very small and very thin with blond curly hair.

'Is this Mr Hennessy's English class?' she asked timidly. Her voice was very low. Almost a whisper.

'Yes,' chorused a few voices.

She closed the door. I looked up and held my breath. 'I am Ms McDwyer. I will be teaching here for a while.'

I glanced outside. It had stopped raining.

'This is my first year teaching,' her quiet voice told us as she smiled across the room

That was her first fatal mistake. Even as she said it I saw the boys' deadpan eyes brighten. Their set mouths curved into smiles. She spoke of the course, of the books we would study, of the things we would do. I was interested. To my utmost surprise, I was inter-ested in English.

'We will begin tomorrow,' she said. 'We have a lot to get through.'

Sometimes when she spoke she stumbled on her words. Self-consciously she kept tucking a curl behind her ear. The boys' eyes sparkled wickedly. They were like tigers watching their prey. Soon they would move in for the kill.

We started the next day. Ms McDwyer was early for class. She was full of enthusiasm. So much so, we thought she would burst.

'We will start with a short story.' There was a lot of meaning and groaning. 'It's called "Old House" and is written by James Brown.'

There was uproar. James Brown must be the most boring, dull writer in the history of mankind. Even his name was boring.

She beamed. 'You will be surprised what you will find in a short story.'

Laughter filled the room. What could possibly be found in a short story?

She was right. We were surprised. There were hidden meanings behind the words, secret messages buried within masked symbols, found only after much uncovering. It was almost as if we were lost in a maze and trying to work our way out. I was so absorbed in my work I did not hear the bell dong drearily throughout the school. Already I was looking forward to the next class.

We started another short story.

'This is called "The Windows of Wonder" and was written by Bryan McMahon,' she informed us. 'Now you can really see the art of the short story.'

I set about it with zest. I used my new-found skills to look behind the text, plunging into murky waters which had not even been paddled before. I could see all too clearly through those windows. I could see 'the yellow sunlight, the silver stars, and the many-coloured wheel of the rainbow'. At the end of the rainbow I could see a blurred figure in the distance. I could see the figure walking towards the colour and reaching out and touching it and suddenly the figure became clear and I could see my own reflection perfectly.

The next day began with poetry. 'John, what would you write about that window?' she asked.

We roared with amusement. It must have been infectious, as she laughed with us.

'Often our most simple images create wonderful poetry,' she told us, misty-eyed.

The window became an amazing mirror seeing it all, the great beauty of nature on one side and the excitement of the classroom on the other. It was a two-headed monster. Nothing was ordinary any more. Everything glinted and shimmered. The words were no longer black and white. They were yellow and purple and red, wavering and contracting, pacing and dancing. Something ignited in me as I mustered all my courage and wrote as I had never written before.

She introduced Library. I soon found myself in fascinating new worlds, which seized me from my normal lifestyle, clasped my imagination, clutched my mind. It was my release. She opened up a whole new world for me. She caught my attention immediately and it never wavered. My head was filled with amazing thoughts which flowed onto paper, complicated stories suddenly became clear. I was a different person.

My classmates were not as easy a conquest. They were in permanent shadow. Her ideas fell on deaf ears, her world of colour remained for them a world of darkness.

After one week the paper fights began. She stopped abruptly, so absorbed in her work she had not at first noticed the small pieces flying across the room.

'Who threw those?'

Nobody answered. She began again haltingly. More paper was thrown as she wrote on the board, followed by grunting noises. The classroom began to fill up with little scrunched-up pieces. They were almost like snowballs. She asked Michelle to pick them up. Her voice was barely audible.

'Stop that now or I will give the whole class extra homework.' She took a deep breath and began again. The last paper was thrown and a grunting sound was made. She gave the class extra homework.

The weeks slowly drifted by. They were a disaster. Every day they thought of something different – crude remarks written on the board, notes being passed, ink on her chair, dusters mysteriously disappearing. She dealt out punishments which were never completed, threatened visits to the headmaster which never happened, and tried miserably to keep the class in order, but failed.

I tried my best. I ignored the fights and yells and noises in the class. I strained my ears to listen to every word she said. She praised my work. I was exuberant. English was not learning any more. It was fun. Magic was created in our classroom. Sparks flew between our four walls each day. I longed and longed for English period, watched in vain as it flew by and hated when it was over. When Ms McDwyer was teaching, she stopped stumbling and fixing her hair. It was almost as if she stepped onto a stage and into another role. But each time she became more confident there would be another fight or missing copybook, and her new-found confidence would diminish before our eyes as she turned into a crumbling heap once again.

The boys were getting restless. Notes on the board and missing dusters were nothing exciting. They wanted something that would really get to her. They racked their brains trying to think. What was the key to her fear? Then it clicked. It was like a sudden clearing on a rainy day. And they probably would not even get into trouble. It was foolproof. I panicked.

I tried to stand up to them. Their rows of smirking faces and smug grins proved too much for me. Adam stood out clearest of all. His brown eyes shone brightly against the rest. He was smiling. A special smile. Just like the way he smiled at Sarah. I could not do it.

She came into class as usual the following day and closed the door gently. She chattered for a while, the usual remarks about current affairs and the weather. She asked us if we had heard about a young girl's work being published in the local newspaper, the winning entry in the library competition. There was no answer. She asked Adam a question. Silence. She gave a nervous laugh. If it were anyone else they would have ignored it. She fell right into their childish trap. The pressure had been building up for months. It was time for breaking point. She did not know what to do. She was so shy she simply could not handle it. She tried talking, she tried pleading, she tried extra homework. She had tried them all before. She even tried raising her voice.

I kept quiet and watched. I could have done something. I did nothing.

She surprised us all. It came out in a flood of tears. Then she fled. Anger tore through me like a steam engine. I was so enraged that at first speech was impossible. I regained my senses when my self-control finally snapped.

'How could you?' I shouted. 'How could you do that to her? How could you make her cry?'

They all stared back at me. Rows and rows of unfriendly faces. They seemed endless. Shock was their first reaction. Then they smiled. They had won. I felt sick. Nausea welled up inside me until I thought I would burst. I suddenly felt light on my feet and dizzy. I was spinning and the white walls seemed to be closing in around me. Nothing was real any more.

Adam spoke first. His voice brought me back. Reality hit me sharply. He wasn't smiling any more. The sparkle had left his eyes. 'We weren't the only ones,' he mumbled.

I could not sleep that night. Adam was right. I could have done something. I would tomorrow. I would apologise and talk even if no one else would. It was funny how I did not care about what the class thought any more. Everything had changed. A picture of her face, eyes brimming with tears, came into my mind's eye. I tossed and turned.

The morning dawned bright and early. I was in school long before the bell. English seemed an eternity in coming. It came and went. She never showed. The next day was the same, the one after no different. I asked when she was coming back and was told she was sick. I stopped studying. I stopped sleeping. Guilt was slowly but surely eating me up. After a week my greatest fear rose up to greet me face-to-face when a younger version of Mr Hennessy strode into the room and slammed the door behind him. He took his seat and surveyed us like a lord over his tenants. He looked out-of-place, much too big and bulky after the small figure of Ms McDwyer. His movements were clumsy, his voice soft with menace. He wrote Mr O'Toole on the board in block letters.

'I have been teaching for years and believe me I have met a lot worse than the likes of you. Open your books at page seventy-four.'

I stared down at my short story and tried to concentrate. Even though his voice was low it seemed to vibrate and bounce off the walls. The words no longer skipped and jumped and danced, calling me to join them. They remained flat on the desk, printed starkly in black and white. The hidden meanings were lost forever in a tidal wave of guilt. Distracted, I looked around the classroom. The boys' faces were deadpan. Outside, the rain was falling softly.

Exteriors

C A I T R Í O N A   F I T Z S I M O N S

Appearances are nothing
but the hard shiny shell of an egg,
the gloss on a fingernail,
concealing the true colours of what is within.
You must take the time to crack the egg,
gently, without spilling the contents,
remove the polish
without chipping the nail.
The trouble is,
some people prefer shiny eggs
and glossy nails.

Bones

SARA-JANE DEVENNEY

Did you know that when full grown
You have 206 bones all of your own?
In our skull we have 29
To protect our brain and mind;
We have 32 bones in our arm
To shield our friends and us from harm;
In our leg there are 31
These help us run and play, for fun;
Our spine is known to have 26 bones
If you hurt these you would just groan.

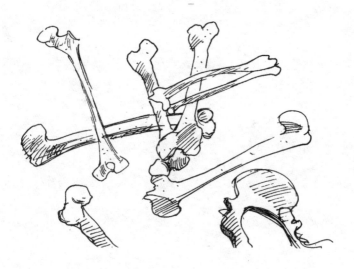

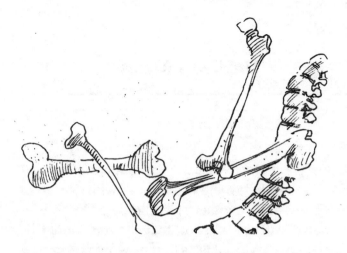

Without these bones we would look a sight,
We would never be able to stand upright.
We would roll about like a blob of jelly,
Just take a look down at your belly.
But with only bones we wouldn't look right,
If you saw us out you would get a fright;
So to cover them up – all 206
We have fibres, ligaments, muscles and flesh.
Oh! What a mix!

The Bee's Knees

ÁINE MAGEE

The sun crept slowly, silently, through a crack and suddenly the whole room was flooded with rich, golden light revealing another splendid day. Queen Beatrice noted with satisfaction that the day would be perfect for her loyal subjects to start work on her new task. She shivered in anticipation of what success would mean. But she couldn't bring herself to think of the consequences if they should fail.

No, all thoughts of failure were far from her mind. She wrapped her royal robe, which was the customary yellow and black colours, around her and buzzed happily into the hive headquarters to tell her subjects what to do. Her thoughts were dominated by happy plans, plans of what she could do when the task was completed. Although she knew that her job was to oversee the gathering of pollen for her winter supplies and that she was neglecting her duty as queen and as ruler of all the bees in Sunshine Street, she couldn't resist the plan.

All her life Queen Beatrice had dreamt of becoming queen because once she had achieved this she knew there would be no stopping her. Once she had power, she could achieve her lifelong ambition, her secret

dream, her only wish and desire. The desire that had burned deep inside her during her every waking moment and dominated her dreams when she slept. The desire to be equal with humans. To become like a human!

She buzzed happily thinking of the endless possibilities that would exist if only she were human. To walk, to run, to dance, to skip. Oh, how she longed to run along with the little children who often came playing around her tree. To jump with them, to hop. But Queen Beatrice knew it was impossible. She would never be able to join in their games as she couldn't run or use her legs. And all because of one minor factor: she had *no knees*.

But Queen Beatrice had found a way to deal with this problem. After all, knees had to originate somewhere. Somewhere, there must be a spare pair of knees waiting to be claimed. So her subjects would just have to find this somewhere and get those knees.

'Silence!' she commanded as her subjects gathered in the hive headquarters. A hush descended on the room and all the bees bowed to their queen. 'Hmmm,' she cleared her throat with authority, 'well, as you all know by now,' she beamed down at the hundreds of bees before her, 'today I have a very important job for you to do. Today you will begin your search for knees. Once you find them you must report immediately to me. Soon we will no longer be inferior to humans. Soon we will be equal. Soon we will have knees.'

The bees cheered loudly and clapped their wings together in tremendous applause. They were overcome by the excitement of the queen's speech and of their fellow bees' enthusiasm, and they were eager to set out on their mission.

Bees are not lazy creatures. They always work without stopping until their various jobs are done. And this job was no different from gathering pollen. In fact, many saw it as easier than that tiresome task. It would be easy-beesy to find knees – or so the bees thought. They were soon to discover it wasn't as easy as it seemed.

The bees set out in pairs and searched everywhere.

For miles they were seen hunting high and low. They flew bravely through thick thorn bushes, getting severely scratched in search of those knees. They risked their lives peeping into birds' nests where they could easily be gobbled up by their enemies, the birds. They dived into rivers, flew through clouds and when night came some adventurous bees even tried to reach the moon, feeling sure that the knees would be there.

After three days of nonstop searching, the bees were very tired, really hungry and completely discouraged. Their queen, too, shared these feelings. She had paced up and down in headquarters, refusing to eat or sleep since she had sent the bees on their mission. And as every hour passed, she grew angrier and angrier and the path she made on the floor got blacker and blacker. Now, as she stood before her subjects she was fuming.

'You lazy bees!' she shouted. 'You selfish, self-centred, disloyal bees. I gave you an order. And I expected it to be carried out. But yet, you defy me and return here empty-handed. You couldn't even complete this simple task.' She caught her breath. 'You couldn't even find *one* pair of knees!'

She was about to launch into another speech when there was a terrible crash and bump – and then the dreadful sound of a child crying filled the air. The bees flew outside, their hearts filled with sorrow for the child who sounded in so much pain. There, sitting on the grass was a little girl. Her eyes were filled with tears as she sat in a pool of blood.

The queen forgot her bad mood and flew to the girl, ordering two bees to dry the child's tears. 'What's the matter?' she asked the sobbing girl.

The girl stopped crying abruptly, and gazed at the queen who was looking at her kindly. 'You spoke!' she said, amazed.

'Yes, my dear, all animals can talk,' the queen replied, 'except not many humans take the time to listen. Now, tell me what's wrong.'

The girl showed the queen her knees, which were cut and bruised and bleeding. 'I fell,' she explained. 'I hate knees. Whenever I play or run, I always end up falling and cutting them. They're such a nuisance.'

The queen and all her subjects were so amazed they could hardly speak.

'But ... but ... we are looking for knees to be able to run and jump and skip and ...'

The girl was shocked. 'You *want* knees! But I hate them. I would much prefer to be able to fly, like you

can. Then I couldn't hurt myself.'

Suddenly a lookout bee called: 'Someone's coming!' It was the girl's mother who called her home.

The bees returned to the hive headquarters. They expected the queen to take up her lecture again, but instead she said: 'Call off the search for the knees. We don't want those ugly things that get hurt so easily. We have wings which are much better. And much safer. So, call off the search. Bees don't need and don't want *knees*.'

Mission to Mars

PÁDRAIC GLYNN

DAY ONE

This was a great day in the history of space travel – the first manned mission to Mars. Back in late 1993, a scientist had invented an engine that could get a ship to Mars in only two hours. The name of the ship was the Glynnsir (named after me). The captain of the ship was myself, Pádraic J Glynn. My second-in-command was John Moloney, the navigators were Martin O'Rourke and Declan Maguire and the science officer was Brian Keehan. I also controlled communications. As a special treat, we had an admiral aboard. His name was Damien Martin. We were awaiting orders to leave from Mission Control in Shannon. I hoped this would succeed without incident. End of report.

Pádraic Joseph Glynn
Captain

DAY TWO

Today was the worst day ever! We had just arrived at Mars and were about to make an orbit of the planet when the programming for the Mars landing went suddenly wonky and the Glynnsir was flung out of orbit, shooting straight through the solar system and coming slowly to a stop above some strange planet.

We were still trying to figure out what happened.

'Maybe the computer malfunctioned,' said Declan.

'No!' said John angrily. 'The computer system is foolproof. Maybe we went through a black hole.'

Then Damien said, 'There are no black holes beyond Mars. Besides, we were flung through the solar system.'

'Maybe a fuse in the circuitry blew,' suggested Martin, 'and we were flung out of the system seconds after the explosion.'

'That's one possibility, Martin,' I said.

Suddenly a voice came over the intercom: 'This is

the voice of the Kellyons. You are under arrest for violation of our most important rule: No travelling through our galaxy! It is forbidden to do so!'

'Where are we and who is speaking?' I said.

The voice came on again: 'This is the voice of the King of Kellyon. You are above the planet Kellyon. You will be sucked through our atmosphere in a few minutes. On our planet you will learn of your punishment. Transmission ends now.'

We were all stunned. We had never heard of space travel being forbidden.

'Brian, what is the atmosphere of this planet made of?' I asked. Brian typed the question into his computer and when he got the answer he was surprised. 'The atmosphere is just like ours – carbon dioxide and oxygen!' We were all amazed at this. An atmosphere just like ours! Then the ship began to rock and shudder.

'What's happening?' Declan cried in horror.

'We're being pulled through the atmosphere of the planet!' said Martin at the navigation controls. It was true. We were pulled right through the planet's atmosphere and landed on the surface with a crash.

After a few moments, the hatch doors of the ship opened and three aliens appeared in the hatchway. To our horror the aliens looked just like Michael Kelly. They were armed with laser guns. One of them said: 'You are under arrest. Come with us please and no funny tricks.' We were led out of the craft one by one. Much to our relief the ship was undamaged.

The planet outside was very different to Earth. The

ground was red with pink stripes. The buildings on the planet were square with triangular doors. The people all looked like Michael Kelly, and there were no children or women on the planet.

We heard a humming noise ahead of us. A hatch in one of their spaceships was opening. A man dressed in robes and who also looked like Michael Kelly appeared and a voice from the back of the spaceship boomed out: 'The Grand King of Kellyon is here. Kneel and obey his asking.' Everyone on the planet obeyed this command. The King smiled, then raised his hands for silence. He frowned and began to speak: 'We have six criminals in our midst. They have disobeyed the most important law of all – the law of not travelling into our galaxy. These six have disobeyed it so they must be punished. They will be taken to the swamp of Kellyon at Kellya and thrown into it ...' At this point I could bear no more. I ran off into the crowd. As I left the crowd behind me, I tripped and fell. Then I woke in my own bed. It had only been a dream.

Pádraic Joseph Glynn
Captain!

* * *

AFTER THE DREAM

I think I will have to go and see a shrink. When I told my mother about the dream she just laughed. I told Mrs de Buitléir about the dream when I got to school, and she sent me out of the classroom for giving her cheek.

Daniel Madigan said to me: 'You must be going

crazy, Pádraic. Will you go and see a doctor?' Imelda and Assumpta also told me to see a doctor.

John Moloney was on my side though: 'Don't worry, Pádraic, I believe you.' Maureen was also on my side.

I went into a shrink's office on the way home. His name was Doctor Screwlooski. When I told him about the dream, he said I was probably reading too much science fiction. I was, too. I was reading a sience fiction story the night before.

Me

ANDREW TOFT

I am bones and skin
and organs within
and blood and veins
and bowels and brains
and lungs that suck
and fists that puck
and toes that wriggle
and mouths that giggle
and tongues that talk
and feet that walk
and ears that hear
and heights I fear
and minds that think
and eyes that wink
and hearts that break
and hands that make
and clothes I wear
and styles in my hair
and posters on the wall
and friends tall and small
and what you get is what you see
and what you get is always me.

Contributors
(Note: age given is at the date of submission)

A Poem Switch by Grace Lynch. Grace is 10 years old, lives in Ardee, Co Louth, and goes to Stabannon National School, Castlebellingham, Co Louth.

My Sister Judy by Davey Kelleher. Davey is 5 years old, lives in Rathfarnham, Dublin, and goes to St Mary's National School, Rathfarnham.

The Supreme Decorator by Jonathan Mullin. Jonathan is 15 years old. He lives in Kilmaine, Co Mayo, and goes to Ballinrobe Community School.

Damhán Alla by Nadine Ní Scannláin. Nadine is 7 years old, lives in Leitir Ceanainn, Co Donegal, and attends Gaelscoil Adhamhnáin in Leitir Ceanainn.

Chernobyl by Aifric Mac Aodha. Aifric is 14 years old, lives in Cnoc Mhuirfean, Dublin, and goes to Coláiste Íosagáin in Dublin.

Planet Tron by Ciara Bardon. Ciara is 11 years old. She lives in Terenure, Dublin, and goes to Presentation Primary Convent, Terenure.

Diary of a War Horse by Peter Hughes. Peter is 10 years old, lives in Castlebar, Co Mayo, and attends Snugboro National School, Castlebar.

The Troll by Michael Patten. Michael is 11 years old, lives in Westport, Co Mayo, and goes to Tonragee National School in Co Mayo.

The Mechanical Drawing Poem by Geoffrey Gray. Geoffrey is 14 years old, lives in Churchtown, Dublin, and goes to Wesley College, Dublin.

Ionsaí Ningach by Dara de Búrca. Dara is 13 years old, lives in Carlow, and goes to Presentation College, Carlow.

Light by Ruth Morrissey. Ruth is 14 years old. She lives in Kilcoole, Co Wicklow, and goes to Loreto Secondary School, Bray, Co Wicklow.

The Orchard by Eimear McNally. Eimear is 14 years old, lives in Carrigaline, Co Cork, and attends Carrigaline Community School.

The Bee Story by Stephen O'Brien. Stephen is 6 years old, lives in Templeogue, Dublin and goes to St Pius' National School, Terenure, Dublin.

A Glorious Victory by James Bowen. James is 14 years old, lives in Kinsale, Co Cork, and goes to Presentation Brothers College, Cork.

Fat Cat by Niamh Reilly. Niamh is 5 years old, lives in Ballina, Co Mayo, and goes to Scoil Croí Ró-Naofa, Ballina.

Braces by Linda Murphy. Linda is 15 years old, lives in Castleconnell, Co Limerick, and attends St Mary's Secondary School, Newport, Co Tipperary.

My Grandad Frank's Day by Karen Leonard. Karen is 13 years old. She lives in Kilcormac, Co Offaly, and goes to Kilcormac Vocational School.

The Fight by Andrew Toft. Andrew is 15 years old, lives in Carrigaline, Co Cork, and goes to Carrigaline Community School.

My Daddy by Fergus Monnelly. Fergus is 5 years old, lives in Foxrock, Dublin, and goes to St Patrick's National School, Foxrock.

My Baby Sister by Benjamin Breen. Benjamin is 11 years old, lives in Castlebar, Co Mayo, and attends Ballyheane National School, Castlebar.

Old by Maude Fahy. Maude is 10 years old, lives in Tuam, Co Galway, and goes to Presentation Primary School, Tuam.

Snow White and the Seven Dwarfs by Sara Hayes. Sara is 12 years old, lives in Montenotte, Cork, and goes to Scoil Mhuire Banríon, Mayfield, Cork.

Crann by Gemma Blanche. Gemma is 11 years old, lives in Newcastle West, Co Limerick, and goes to Gaelscoil Ó Doghair, Co Limerick.

The Love of My Life by Muireann Prendergast. Muireann is 13 years old, lives in Limerick, and goes to Laurel Hill Coláiste FCJ, Limerick.

Past the Moon by Andrew Toft. This is the second piece from Andrew, who is 15. (See *The Fight*.)

A Narrow Escape by Alice Stack. Alice is 10 years old, lives in Letterbarrow, Co Donegal, and goes to St Peter's National School, Mountcharles, Co Donegal.

The Suppression of Emotion by Mary Smithwick. Mary is 15 years old. She lives in Midleton, Co Cork, and goes to St Mary's High School, Midleton.

The First Day I Went to the Canal by Anne-Marie Cusack. Anne-Marie is 6 years old, lives in Sandymount, Dublin, and goes to Scoil Mhuire, Sandymount.

Seariders by Ionia Ní Chróinín. Ionia is 9 years old, lives in Craughwell, Co Galway, and attends Gael Scoil Dara in Galway.

My Mother's Childhood Memories of Christmas by Deirdre Hayes. Deirdre is 13 years old, lives in Clonakilty, Co Cork, and goes to St Joseph's School, Clonakilty.

The Gambler by Rami Okasha. Rami is 14 years old, lives in Bishopstown, Cork, and goes to Coláiste an Spioraid Naoimh, Bishopstown.

The Winter's Sleep by Karen Rochford. Karen is 10 years old, lives in Tallaght, Dublin, and goes to St Anne's Senior School in Dublin.

A Day in the Life of a Full Stop by Peter Callanan. Peter is 15 years old. He lives in Craughwell, Co Galway, and goes to Clongowes Wood College, Naas, Co Kildare.

Quiet as Mice by Anne-Marie Barry. Anne-Marie is 13 years old, lives in Athy, Co Kildare, and goes to Scoil Mhuire, Athy.

Seagull's First Flight by Sarah Hickey. Sarah is 11 years old, lives in Blackrock, Co Louth, and goes to St Oliver Plunkett National School, Blackrock.

Bart Simpson by Séamus de Nais. Séamus is 11 years old, lives in Caisleán Nua Thiar, Co Limerick, and attends Gaelscoil Ó Doghair, Co Limerick.

My Winter by Brendan Jackson. Brendan is 15 years old. He lives in Kilternan, Co Dublin, and goes to Wesley College, Dublin.

History by Mary Smithwick. This is the second piece from Mary who is 15. (See *The Suppression of Emotion*.)

My Nanny by Lisa Carthy. Lisa is 11 years old. She lives in Carraig on Bannow, Co Wexford, and goes to St Mary's National School, Carraig on Bannow.

Shattered by Cathy Toft. Cathy is 15 years old, lives in Carrigaline, Co Cork, and attends Carrigaline Community School.

Bríd na mBrionglóidí by Caoimhe Ní Chomhraí. Caoimhe is 12 years old, lives in Na Forbacha, Co Galway, and goes to Coláiste na Coiribe, Galway.

The Tree by Claire O'Keeffe. Claire is 15 years old, lives in Carrigaline, Co Cork, and goes to Carrigaline Community School.

Song of the Humpbacked Whale by Lois West. Lois is 12 years old, lives in Drinagh, Co Wexford, and attends Scoil Réalt na Mara, Kilmore, Co Wexford.

My Pet by Liam Stewart. Liam is 6 years old. He lives in Shercock, Co Cavan, and attends Shercock National School.

A Day in the Life by Belinda McKeon. Belinda is 14 years old. She lives in Longford, and attends Scoil Mhuire, Longford.

Seanchara by Michelle Lane. Michelle is 12 years old. She lives in Mallow, Co Cork, and attends Kilmagner National School, Fermoy, Co Cork.

Hideaway by Michelle Alexander. Michelle is 15 years old. She lives in Carrigaline, Co Cork, and goes to Carrigaline Community School.

A Day in the Life of a Dead Cabbie by Leslie Carberry. Leslie is 12 years old, lives in Leixlip, Co Kildare, and at-tends Belvedere College, Dublin.

Ms McDwyer by Cathy Toft. This is the second piece from Cathy who is 15. (See *Shattered*.)

Exteriors by Caitríona Fitzsimons. Caitríona is 13 years old, lives in Portmarnock, Co Dublin, and goes to Portmarnock Community School.

Bones by Sara-Jane Devenney. Sara-Jane is 10 years old, lives in Lifford, Co Donegal, and goes to Raphoe Central National School, Co Donegal.

The Bee's Knees by Áine Magee. Áine is 15 years old, lives in Celbridge, Co Kildare, and goes to St Wolstan's Holy Faith Convent, Celbridge.

Mission to Mars by Pádraic Glynn. Pádraic is 14 years old. He lives in Ennis, Co Clare, and goes to St Anne's National School in Ennis.

Me by Andrew Toft. This is a third piece by Andrew who is 15. (See *The Fight* and *Past the Moon*.)